$$N = N_s f_p n_e f_b n_i f_c L_c / L_p$$

—the formula for the probability
of communicating with life on other planets

"There is one thing we can forecast with very high probability. At this moment the sound of astral music from some far-distant world is falling about us. Within our hearing these pulsing, intelligent signals of long ago and far away reach out for recognition beyond the threshold of our consciousness like waves of the eternal sea pounding upon a deserted beach. We can be almost certain that this evidence of other life and other intelligence is here before us if we can only search it out."

from THE SEARCH FOR LIFE ON OTHER WORLDS

Captain David C. Holmes, Assistant Deputy to the Chief of Naval Materiel, has been involved with research and development of guided missiles since 1949. Formerly with the NATO Naval Forces, he was also the manager of Project Shepherd, the military world-wide space tracking network. He is the author of numerous articles and books, including WHAT'S GOING ON IN SPACE?

BANTAM
SCIENCE
AND
MATHEMATICS

The Search
For Life on
Other Worlds

by Captain
David C. Holmes, U.S.N.

BANTAM BOOKS
TORONTO · NEW YORK · LONDON

THE SEARCH FOR LIFE ON OTHER WORLDS
*Bantam Science and Mathematics edition
published April 1967*

*Bantam Books are published by Bantam Books, Inc., a subsidiary
of Grosset & Dunlap, Inc. Its trade-mark, consisting of the words
"Bantam Books" and the portrayal of a bantam, is registered in the
United States Patent Office and in other countries. Marca Registrada.
Bantam Books, Inc., 271 Madison Avenue, New York, N.Y. 10016.*

PRINTED IN THE UNITED STATES OF AMERICA

For Squidge

"This land of Oz is a pretty big place, when you get to all the edges of it."

Dorothy in *The Lost Princess of Oz*

CONTENTS

1 | THE CASE FOR LIFE ON EARTH

We live isolated and alone on a small cinder which orbits a minor star. Until the present age, we have seen the warmth of recognition, the communion of friendship, and the excitement of answering intelligence only on the faces of fellow earth-bound humans. The total of our experience and knowledge is confined within the humble limits of our planet.

Will this always be so?

Perhaps some day we can link hands across the vast reaches of intergalactic space with other creatures whose hopes, fears, ambitions, and capabilities are similar to our own. But are there any others like us in the universe whom we might contact? If there are, how can we go about it?

It is our amazing good fortune to be alive at the first moment in history when the answers to some of these questions are coming within reach.

An article published recently in a German magazine is entitled: "Is Life Possible on the Surface of the Earth?" The author pretended to be a scientist on the planet Jupiter where conditions are much different from those on our own planet. The surface temperature on Jupiter is about minus 130° C., so that water exists only as ice, and the oceans of Jupiter are filled with liquid ammonia. The atmosphere is principally methane. Therefore our mythical Jovian scientist must breathe methane air and drink ammonium water. Intelligent Jovians, training their telescopes on the earth for signs of life, would find that its temperature was extremely hot, that its atmosphere contained no life-giving methane, and that liquid ammonia could not possibly be found on its surface. Inevitably they would conclude, after gathering much data and after

1

a great deal of learned discussion, that the earth was an arid, non-fertile planet, and that "life-as-we-know-it" could not exist here.

Impossible? Yes, in a way. We know, for example, that the carbon, hydrogen, and oxygen of our earth provide a better environment for life than any other we can imagine. We do not believe that there are scientists on Jupiter capable of examining our planet, but this tentative knowledge is based on a very narrow and restricted point of view. The methane-ammonia atmosphere of Jupiter is quite receptive to the formation of life-like molecules, and life substances have been formed in a laboratory under similar conditions. The dense gases around Jupiter may trap the sun's rays so that the surface temperature may not be much more uncomfortable than your living room, although many more Mariner probes remain to be fired before we will know much about the Jovian temperatures.

And then there are some other interesting questions. We, of course, know there is life on the earth, but even on our nearest neighbor, Mars, earth-life would be far from a proven certainty. Our marks and defacements on this planet are more humble than we might like to admit. Even the most powerful telescopes—by earth standards —would be hard put to establish our existence if they were located in Martian observatories.

Our greatest engineering structures would be too insignificant to be seen, or perhaps would be barely on the threshold of visibility. In this they would appear similar to the way the celebrated Martian canals appear to us.

The lights of New York and London might be marginally visible at night. About the only man-made phenomenon easily seen by Martian astronomers would be nuclear explosions. And these are over so quickly that many would never be seen. Those that were would be the focal point of many arguments among astronomers.

An astronomer of Mars might notice seasonal color changes in our planet like those we have observed on the red planet itself. No doubt the Martian scientists would devise many ingenious theories to explain these phenomena, just as we have. A good many of them would surely exclude the possibility of life.

2

The minimum number of stars in the universe is at least 10 followed by 21 zeros, and of these a great many —at least one in a thousand—must have a family of planets somewhat similar to those of our sun.

How many of these planets might have a surface temperature which would encourage the development of life? Surely one in a thousand.

How many of this group would be of the proper size to capture and hold an atmosphere? Again, one in a thousand.

Suppose we assume that our kind of life is the only type that can be expected to flourish and develop into intelligent beings. We are fragile jelly capable of existing only within narrow limits. Even so, at least one in a thousand of this smallest group of planets must surely pass the final test and contain the proper combination of carbon, oxygen, hydrogen, and nitrogen. These elements are needed to provide the protective, nourishing envelope required to support life similar to ours.

In all, even after this ruthless pruning, we are left with hundreds of millions of planets in the universe on which some kind of life is at least possible. Are you beginning to feel just a little less lonely?

Even the most pessimistic handicapper would give you very good odds that somewhere in this vast community there are other intelligent beings who occasionally wonder if they, too, are alone in the universe.

What manner of creatures might there be on other planets? The possibilities defy our imagination. Even such a heavy and noxious gas as fluorine might nourish life, but the creatures living in a fluorine climate would have to be thick-skinned, like reptiles, to withstand the corrosive gas.

Animals on a large, heavy planet would probably be squat and powerful, crawling on all fours because of the strong pull of gravity. A water-covered planet could produce only fish-like creatures. Inhabitants of a small earth would be long-stemmed and fragile, due to the softer pull of gravity. They would also have wide nostrils and huge lungs to breathe thin atmosphere of a world with little weight. One might expect a greater number of

3

birds on a small sphere, since flight would be such an easy and economical way to get around.

In the universe there are no doubt many other mutations produced by specialized environments, just as there are a variety of characters to be found at a race track. On the other hand, it is quite likely that we will someday discover in outer space someone quite man-like. We are the product of a precise and inexorable selection system—the survival of the fittest. Similar conditions on other worlds may very possibly produce a creature similar to man.

How will we first contact life on other worlds? The tale of our search to establish communications with other life makes one of the truly fascinating detective stories of all time. It contains the classic elements of suspense, mystery, and surprise to a degree worthy of the finest modern thriller. In addition, the attempt to make contact with other intelligent beings will have a deep and lasting significance for all of us.

The most direct means of meeting our astral neighbors would be to climb into a space ship and go and visit them. We have already sent probing rockets around the solar system. When the spidery spacecraft Mariner II flashed across the face of the planet Venus on December 14, 1962, it had accomplished one of the most exciting voyages in human history. For the first time, man had reached out into distant space to unlock some of the secrets of another planet. The Mariner IV voyage around Mars was an even more dramatic reminder that our solar system was beginning to shrink.

Within the next few years we will personally visit the moon. After that trip the planets will be only one small stair step away.

Unfortunately, as we will see later, the moon and the planets of our solar system do not offer many possibilities as promising homes for intelligent life. Mars will perhaps display some life of a low order, while the others may be as sterile as hospital operating rooms before the patient is wheeled in.

We must look further afield. And as soon as we start thinking of this, alas, we quickly realize how small we are and how lacking in capability and time.

4

The heavens are incredibly vast, and our span of life is pitifully short. The nearest star, Alpha Centauri, is more than four light years away from us, but this statement does not provide us with any real perspective of that enormous distance.

Suppose we assume the sun to be about the size of a golf ball. Then the earth would be about the size of a period on this printed page, about 12 feet away from our golf-ball sun. The planets Mars and Venus would be other periods several feet from us. Jupiter would be 50 feet away at its nearest approach. But even in this sub-miniaturized universe, Alpha Centauri is 600 miles away! Most of the group of stars which could support life and which we might be able to contact in this century are more than 2,000 miles away.

Interstellar space contains many terrors which are very real, unlike the sea dragons that inhabited the dreams of Columbus' sailors. These dangers will be difficult to overcome, and many of them are unknown to us even now. But the barrier which appears truly insurmountable is the wall of distance. This formidable obstacle of space will hold us within our solar system far more securely than the chains of gravity which presently confine us to this planet.

There are perhaps ten stars within ten light years of the earth whose size and brightness indicate that they might mother life-bearing planets. Let us plan a trip to one of these for some future space-Magellan.

Because of the vast distances involved, a rocket ship must travel at a speed almost equal to that of light if it is to reach even the nearest star within the useful lifetime of one man—about 99 per cent of the speed of light would be fast enough. A rocket ship must also speed up and slow down. Stopping in space requires a huge amount of energy, and is an almost incredibly complicated feat.

Let us suppose that our rocket ship must accelerate and decelerate with the same force that gravity exerts upon us. This is probably a reasonable assumption, because a human would be most comfortable living in an environment where his weight was the same as it is on the earth. (As a matter of fact, man may not be able to survive for long periods under conditions where the pull of gravity is much higher than on the earth.) It happens that an acceleration of one g (equal to the earth's gravitational force) for a period of about one year will give our space ship the speed of light.

How long will it take to make a voyage to the vicinity of a star ten light years away? That depends on your point of view. For our Magellan's wife back on earth, 24 years would go by before she would see her husband again. But Einstein's theory suggests that for the ship's crew only ten years would have passed! As you can see, space travel is not likely to become very popular with wives if their husbands are going to return looking much younger than they themselves do.

Otherwise the situation appears rather promising—at least at first glance. We will certainly find adventuresome explorers who are willing to devote ten years to such an important and significant endeavor. Now all we need do is build a rocket ship capable of this sort of flight, load it with sufficient fuel, and get on with the project.

It is when we face the problem of fuel that we realize we are in trouble. The most potent source of power which we can imagine today would be a perfect nuclear fusion engine that could change hydrogen to helium. The exhaust velocity of the gases would be about 23,000 feet per second, and it would be a fantastically efficient system by today's standards.

There is one problem. Several million tons of this best of all fuels would be required to propel a rocket ship of even modest size to a star ten light years away. Additional millions of tons would be needed to bring it home again.

Since we are dreaming, there is another conceivability: an engine whose fuel is 50 per cent matter and 50 per cent anti-matter. Such a fuel would theoretically combine to produce pure energy, without any residue whatever. So far, anti-matter exists only briefly in the laboratory, and we haven't the slightest idea of how to build an anti-matter engine. But it is still the most efficient propulsion that we can conceive of. How large must such a rocket be to transport a space ship to a star ten light years away? One of about 500,000 tons might provide a one-way ticket. Our space ship must still weigh as much as six Queen Mary's!

There are numerous side problems to be faced by anyone who wishes to make such a trip. A good deal of shielding is required from both the products of the rocket engine and from the waste matter of space. During the first hours of the flight it would even be necessary to shield the earth from the powerful radiation of such a rocket.

There is at least one other very good reason why we will not go dashing off to other stars with abandon. Suppose we decided to send just one future John Glenn to the nearest star when we feel that we have solved the technical problems. What will this mean in terms of manpower and materials? A fusion rocket which converts hydrogen to helium must weigh a billion times as much as our astronaut. If he weighed only 100 pounds the rocket would still gross 100 billion pounds, or about as much as 750 nuclear carriers like the U. S. S. "Enterprise."

A Cape Kennedy launching facility about the size of the State of Florida would be required to lift our one-man craft off the earth. Even in mass production new Enterprises cost a quarter of a billion dollars each, so the price tag for such an undertaking would run about $200 billion, or almost one-third of our total yearly national production. And this is only a one-way trip! We would still have to pay for a return ticket for our astronaut.

There will never be truly economy-class space travel. Even first-class will likely be far beyond our means for some time to come. Many pages of the Congressional Record will be devoted to the subject before we can hope to get approval for a space-travel project to visit stars. Today, our total space program accounts for something less than one per cent of our total national production.

It may be that we are confined forever to the limits of our solar system. Perhaps this is why we have not been contacted by visiting space ships—if you are willing to discount the rash of flying-saucer reports of the past few years. Even civilizations much more advanced than ours may not have been able to surmount the great barrier of space which separates the suns.

7

On the other hand, perhaps we should not blithely discount all possibilities for interstellar travel. After all, we are only humble beginners in this adventure. Who knows, perhaps we have been visited many times in the past by travelers from outer space. History and mythology are replete with tales of strange visitations. Perhaps these past explorers found our planet so poor and our existence so primitive that they had no further interest in us. We may be like the dusty goods hidden away in a dark corner of the shop where the customers peer briefly and then hurry on.

In any event, the main thing at first is to establish contact with other intelligent life. Fortunately, it is not necessary to travel at all in order to communicate. We can do so, much more practically and almost as effectively without leaving the protection of our own planet.

How will we first discover life on other worlds? We will probably do so by allowing *them* to discover *us*. The way we'll do this is to listen for their radio signals.

There is one thing we can forecast with very high probability. At this moment the sound of astral music from some far-distant world is falling about us. Within our hearing these pulsing, intelligent signals of long ago and far away reach out for recognition beyond the threshold of our consciousness like waves of the eternal sea pounding upon a deserted beach. We can be almost certain that this evidence of other life and other intelligence is here before us if we can only search it out.

And this is a method we can afford, in terms of both energy and time. In order to take advantage of it, all we need to do is listen and have patience. The radio telescopes which are required for this effort are expensive and complicated to build. We certainly have not reached the pinnacle of our knowledge, even though our receiving equipment is highly developed.

Soon we will not only be able to receive, but we will also be able to speak with our own electronic voices, and interstellar communication will become a reality. It will be relatively cheap. Using the best radio transmitters, the highest power, and the largest antennas available, the cost of sending a 50-word telegram to nearby stars would be less than five cents. At this rate we could send the Encyclopedia Britannica for something less than $1,000,000. The Britannica Corporation might even be willing to foot the whole bill as part of their advertising budget.

At this moment we represent only the accumulated history of our planet. Perhaps more accurately, we are the product of its recorded history if one is willing to discount the faded and incomplete contribution of a few ancient bones, a minor pottery collection, and the dim hieroglyphics which can be found on the walls of some old caves. What we know of culture, of art, and of the universal laws of science has been slowly and painfully developed by a few of our more enquiring minds working during a small segment of total earth time.

Our knowledge is hard-won and far from complete. The farther we advance up the tower of discovery, the more we are aware of the great unexplored darkness which lies ahead. Suppose we could suddenly double or triple this accumulated experience by communicating with the intelligence of another civilization which is further along than our own. What a great leap forward that would be! Instead of merely being the product of our own humble growth, we might have available the recorded history of two, and perhaps ultimately, several more planets. Who can guess what wealth of discovery would become ours?

Overnight we might have a cure for cancer and the common cold. Our newly acquired friends might tell us of automobiles and washing machines far more efficient than any we have learned to build.

Perhaps the greatest gains would be social and political. Who knows, possibly we could even learn to survive in a paradoxical age in which, after being fighters from the very beginning, we suddenly arrived at the point where we could no longer afford to fight at all.

There are many, many advantages to having cultured friends at so great a distance. We need never fear that they will want to bury us. Diplomatic treaties will not

9

be necessary, nor will their political leaders be required to make portentous statements of policy with one ear tuned to the voices of a critical constituency.

The great barrier of space will free us forever from the threat of their atomic bombs and they will require no BMEWS (Ballistic Missile Early Warning Systems) to guard against ours. For the first time in our short history we will be able to give our friendship, totally and unequivocally. We need not thrust and parry with such terms as "peaceful coexistence" or "friendly competition." Nature has already provided the restraints. In spite of ourselves, we will be forced to maintain our party manners.

The search for life on other worlds must rank as the most dramatic and exciting human adventure of all time. It is a mature activity which is not likely to bring immediate headlines or a favored position in the cold war. But surely no other activity has a potential for greater human enrichment. The mountain lies before us. Not to climb is unthinkable. As John Glenn said as he left the launch pad for the historic flight of Friendship VII: "We are ready . . . the clock is running . . . all systems are go."

2 | ARE FLYING SAUCERS VISITORS FROM SPACE?

No phenomenon in recent years has been capable of producing more emotional response than flying saucers. If you want a good argument, it is only necessary to bring up the subject, and people immediately choose sides. The resulting discussions have been known to go on all night.

The number and variety of flying saucer tales rival those of ghost story folklore. There are people who say they have talked with the little green astronauts who are supposed to guide the saucers on their long dark journeys. Some say that saucer spacemen have asked

10

them for directions just like any other tourists. There are others who claim they have been taken for short rides by agreeable and friendly saucer operators.

Generally speaking, there are two basic views when it comes to Unidentified Flying Objects, or UFO's as the saucers are officially called. Many people don't believe in them, and hold the view that they are the product of group hallucinations or natural phenomena. Since most flying saucer incidents have been reported at night, often in the wee hours of the morning, some feel that UFO reports are often the product of over-indulgence in strong drink. Those who think this way have a certain amount of official backing for their view. During the April, 1966, Congressional hearings on the military budget, the subject of flying saucers came up and General James Ferguson, Deputy Chief of the Air Force for Research and Development, presented the Air Force view of the subject. He stated that there have been 10,147 reported UFO sightings since 1947. Of these, 9,501 had been identified and explained as natural phenomena. He then went on to say that "The remaining 646 reported sightings are those in which the information was not sufficient to serve as a basis for any useful analysis."

Those on the other side of the argument can also marshal an impressive weight of fact and opinion on their side of the ledger. Numerous scientists of international repute have stated that they believe saucers are of ex-traterrestrial origin and that they represent the work of some far-away superhuman intelligence. Among these is Dr. Walter Riedel, once head of design at the German rocket center at Peenemünde. Dr. Riedel has kept records of UFO sightings over a period of years and has said that he feels they are definitely of extraterrestrial origin and represent the efforts of a high level intelligence. He says: "I am completely convinced that they have an out-of-world basis."

Partisans of this view often contend that the U.S. Air Force and the government are engaged in a great conspiracy to keep the true facts from the general public. They argue that the Air Force has shrouded the whole matter behind a cloak of secrecy and has distorted and misrepresented the facts in order to gloss over the true

11

nature of these visitors from other planets. Perhaps they will even quote the rumor that somewhere in Wright-Patterson Air Force Base there are hidden away the embalmed bodies of several small humanoid figures who were allegedly pulled from the wreckage of a space craft which crashed in the South West a few years ago.

What are the true facts? There can be no doubt that a significant number of sober, honest, responsible, and in many cases knowledgeable, observers have seen *something*.

The first postwar UFO's to make national headlines were seen over Washington State by a private pilot named Kenneth Arnold on June 24, 1947. Arnold was making a short flight from Chehalis to Yakima in the western part of the state when he saw a geese-like formation of flying objects in a long line over Mt. Rainier, a peak which rises spectacularly over 14,000 feet above the surrounding countryside. He was able to follow the flight of these objects for several minutes and later reported them to the local Yakima papers who dutifully passed the story to the national wire services. At one point he described them as saucer-like things, and the name stuck.

After the publicity of this first sighting, the reports began to pour in like bills around the first of the month. "Flying Saucers" rapidly became a household term.

Although no authority has ever considered that UFO's were a threat to humans, a tragedy grew out of one of the early sightings. On January 7, 1948, Air Force Captain Thomas F. Mantell was flying in formation with two other F-51 fighter pilots when he sighted a peculiar object high in the air over Fort Knox, Kentucky. Over the radio, he said it looked like a strawberry ice cream cone. He broke off from his comrades and followed his stratospheric ice cream cone up to an altitude of about 20,000 feet and then disappeared. Later in the day, parts of his aircraft were found scattered over a wide area. Ironically, in retrospect it appears that Captain Mantell was actually chasing a research balloon and apparently lost consciousness from lack of oxygen.

Although scarcely a week has passed in recent years without at least one saucer report, they often seem to appear in batches. The latter half of 1965 and early months of 1966 produced more than their fair share of UFO phenomena.

One of the more interesting incidents occurred about 12 miles from Ann Arbor, Michigan late in March, 1966, near the farm of Frank Mannor. About 8 o'clock one Sunday night Mannor's six dogs began barking all at the same time. Mannor looked out his front door and noticed a faint red glow in the vicinity of some swamp land to the east of his house. He called to his 19-year-old son Ronnie, and the two men went to investigate. Mannor said later that he thought at first a meteor had landed in the swamp and perhaps they could find some of the pieces of it.

As they approached the swamp, they automatically kept silent from their long years of experience as deer hunters. Suddenly, as they climbed a small rise, they came upon a peculiar object about the size of an automobile only a few hundred yards away. It had a green light at one end and a white light at the other. Sure enough, as they got closer they could see that it looked like a flat dish-like object riding about 8 feet above the surface of the ground in a patch of mist. It was a dull blue-grey color with a rough and pitted outer surface like "coral rock," Mr. Mannor said.

As they watched, it suddenly began to glow with a blood-red fluorescence. "Look at that horrible thing, Dad!" shouted Ronnie. Immediately the lights went out. They ran toward it as fast as they could, but when they got there it had vanished.

Back at the house, the dogs were still barking, and Mrs. Mannor had also seen the "thing." She decided to call the police. There are seven other parties on the Mannors' party phone line so that when she called, she told a great many people besides the police. "We've got an object that looks just like what they call a flying saucer," she told them. "It's down in the swamp and it's covered with lights."

In short order, a great many people drove up in their cars and were soon slogging around in the marsh near the Mannors' house. Some 50 of them were rewarded for their efforts and caught a glimpse of the saucer or its after-glow. A good many felt like Deputy Sheriff Stanley McFadden of Washtenaw County who said later: "I seen it—but I still don't believe it!"

A police patrolman, Robert Hunawill from nearby Dexter Township saw "a strange, lighted object" near his patrol car as he approached the Mannors' farm. In his official report he said: "It had peculiar red and white lights which at times took on a bluish tinge. It dipped and turned over the swamp at an altitude of about 1,000 feet. Finally it was joined by three other similar objects, and then they all flew away."

For some years Dr. J. Allen Hynek, director of Northwestern University's Dearborn Observatory, has been a consultant to the Air Force regarding the flying saucer phenomenon. Because of the spectacular nature of the Mannor sightings and the large number of people who reported seeing these objects, Dr. Hynek soon appeared in Dexter Township and began talking to those who had been in the area during that interesting evening.

When he was interviewed by the press later, Dr. Hynek had this to say: "I feel sure that the people who saw those things are entirely honest and sincere. But I am not willing to guess what they saw."

There have been several reports of UFO sightings that were first triggered by animals. In a recent episode near Pittsburgh, a couple stated that their dog acted very strangely when the UFO was in the vicinity of their house. Normally, this dog was a most friendly animal who became acquainted with strangers rapidly and spent most of its time outdoors. When the saucer appeared, the dog became frightened and disappeared into the house. They found it cowering and whimpering in the cellar. Its hearing seemed to be affected as though it was listening to some high pitched noise beyond the range of human ears.

About 8:30 on the evening of August 19, 1965, Harold Butcher, the 16-year-old son of a farmer who lives about 50 miles south of Niagara Falls, New York, was milking the cows in his father's barn. Harold looked out the window of the barn just as he heard a bull, which was tethered in the field, let out a noise "like I have never heard come from an animal before."

Harold noticed that the bull was bending a metal pipe in its efforts to get away from something, even though it had been tied to the pipe by a rope attached to a ring through its nose.

Then the boy noticed a football-shaped object hovering just above the trees about 500 feet from the barn. Harold described his saucer as about 50 feet long and 20 feet thick. When it moved vertically, the craft emitted a red vapor from the bottom. When it moved laterally, a yellow tail of vapor appeared from one of the ends. As he watched, it seemed to settle down behind a large maple tree and vapor trailed off from the edges. Although the saucer didn't make any loud noises, Harold did notice a faint beeping sound.

He had been listening to a small portable radio while he milked the cows and suddenly he realized that it had been making "a heck of a loud noise like static." Harold ran out of the barn toward the UFO, calling to his mother as he went, since his father wasn't home at the time. Just before he got to the place where the bull was tethered, the saucer shot up from the ground and disappeared into the clouds. Harold said later that the beep-beep sound seemed to grow in intensity as the saucer rose. Meanwhile Mrs. Butcher had noticed a sudden radio interference in the house.

Harold next ran into the kitchen, yelling about his discovery, and almost immediately ran out again with his 14-year-old brother, Robert. The two boys saw the UFO hovering over a grove of trees. Mrs. Butcher and a visiting girl, Kathleen Brougham, came out also, but didn't arrive in time to see anything. Mrs. Butcher went back in the house and called the police.

A few moments later Kathleen Brougham caught sight of the saucer as it moved across a field less than half a mile from the house. She called the others who came out and watched it disappear in the direction of a neighboring town at an altitude of about 1,000 feet. They all agreed that they had seen a faint outline of a football shape, a glowing yellow vapor trail, and a green glow in the clouds above.

The police arrived soon after and the boys took them over the entire area. They reported that a rather pungent odor was in the air at first, but otherwise they found nothing unusual.

15

Not only have flying saucers been seen and photographed, they have also been tracked by radar. One of the more interesting incidents which involved sensory equipment other than mere gullible human eyes occurred during the early morning hours of Sunday, July 20, 1952, in Washington, D.C.

Unlike many of those who have become involved in after-hours capers in our national capital, the people connected with the actions in this one had not been to a single cocktail party. In fact, they were all highly skilled technicians involved in earning their living in a most precise and exacting business.

The first scene took place in the Civil Aeronautics Authority Traffic Control Center at the Washington National Airport. The chief radar operator, Harry Barnes, was supervising the task of directing the heavy air traffic in the vicinity of the capital city. Suddenly, at 12:40 a.m. he heard an exclamation from one of his operators. Going over to the scope, he noticed several strange targets on the screen about 15 miles south of Washington. Barnes immediately sent technicians to check the complicated circuits of his radar equipment. They found everything in proper working order.

By this time the unidentified objects on the cathode-ray screens were performing a weird electronic ballet. They disappeared and reappeared in other places like bathers swimming under water. Some of them circled over the capital city like vultures over a carcass while others moved rapidly from one side of the screen to the other. The operators estimated their speeds as varying from 130 miles per hour up to hundreds of miles per minute. They dipped and turned over the White House and the Pentagon.

Seeking to verify his radar findings, Barnes called various airport control towers around Washington and asked them to search the sky for his targets. A tower operator at Andrews Air Force Base saw a yellow light at a point where Barnes had a target echo. The same strange light was reported by a workman who knew nothing about the radar reports.

Barnes asked the pilot of an airliner to check an area where his radar scopes showed a concentration of these objects. Sure enough, the pilot was able to see them. A radar echo was noticed near a commercial airliner approaching from Richmond. The pilot of this plane could also see a strange yellow object near his path. Air Force jets were vectored out of Andrews to contact the saucers, but they were unable to catch up with them. Gradually, toward morning, the objects disappeared. The following night all was back to normal and no flying saucers appeared.

There have been numerous other reports of electronic interference caused by flying saucers. Not long ago, two patrolmen in Hammond, Indiana, heard a loud, beeping noise on their police radio. At the same time they saw ahead of them a long, metallic object a few hundred feet off the ground. They were able to follow it for some minutes, and after it disappeared the beeping sound stopped.

James W. Stokes, a high altitude research engineer at White Sands Proving Ground saw a football-shaped UFO sweep across the highway in front of his car. Both the motor and the car radio failed at the same time. Just as he was starting up again, the saucer came back, and again his motor and radio stopped working.

Such incidents have not been restricted to the United States. A number of electronic technicians, many of whom were also ham radio operators, noticed an intensely bright saucer over a hill near their tracking station north of Ottawa, Canada. At the same time all signals on their radios were drowned out by a rapidly pulsing tone on one frequency. When the UFO left, the radio reception became normal again.

A vast variety of sizes, shapes and characteristics have been reported among the 10,000-odd UFO sightings. However, a great many seem to fall into definite categories. The shape reported most often is that of a saucer, a disk-like object whose diameter is about 10 times its thickness. These vary in size from 10 feet in diameter to more than 100. Perhaps 60 per cent of all sightings are in this class.

The second most common type of flying saucer is the cigar-shaped or football-like object. These also come in a variety of sizes and configurations.

Beyond these types of saucers, there are the unexplained bright lights which have been seen at night. Many of these change from one color to another as the observers watch. Often several of them are in what appears to be a controlled formation like a flight of military aircraft. Also there are round globes, and cones, and Saturn-like objects with definite rings circling them. But there are not many of these latter types.

The fact that most of these objects are of a saucerlike shape is in itself perhaps significant. A pancake configuration is by no means the best for flight inside the atmosphere. A Buck Rogers cigar shape would offer much less drag and considerably more aerodynamic stability. Once outside the atmospheric cloak, however, the saucer makes a lot more sense. It has many of the structural advantages of a sphere plus a few of its own. In addition it provides a wide, flat surface for absorbing the radiation of nearby stars which it may be able to convert into energy for its own use.

It is also difficult to see how most people could visualize saucer shapes if the whole UFO business were a figment of overworked imaginations. We are used to thinking of flying objects in terms of airplanes, balloons, and rocket shapes. Neither fact nor fiction are likely to implant in us any ideas of saucers flying around.

The reports of sounds emitted by flying saucers are as varied as their shapes. By far the majority are said to proceed on their way silently. However, some are supposed to hum faintly while others sound a distinct beepbeep. Whirring and hissing noises have also been associated with UFO's by some observers. Scientists have agreed, however, that no cases have been reported where the sounds from the saucers were sufficient to account for the fantastic propulsion plants which they must possess if they indeed travel from one planet to another. In fact, all earthly flying vehicles stir up a considerable racket when they are merely hovering over one spot, except for kites and tethered balloons.

One feature which has baffled scientists perhaps more

than any other about flying saucers is their unique motion. Some are said to hover low over the surface, often with a soft undulating motion, while others appear to shimmer like a mirage on a hot day. Most of them have demonstrated the ability to go straight up, down, or sideways almost as though they had never heard of the law of gravity. They appear to be able to change direction at 90-degree angles no matter what speed they are traveling. Their capacity to accelerate from zero to speeds of several miles per second is far beyond that of any man-made flying machine.

A number of scientists have made calculations based on the reported maneuverability of flying saucers and their conclusions are unanimous—earthly materials and earthly creatures could not stand the pressures which they develop. After one 90-degree turn at even a relatively low speed such as 100 miles per hour, all human astronauts in such a craft would have been flattened lifelessly against the walls.

What is the official government view of all these reports and sightings?

During the April, 1966, congressional hearings on the military budget, General Ferguson was asked a number of questions about flying saucers. He stated that the U.S. Air Force has had the responsibility since 1947 of examining all UFO reports "to determine if there is a threat to the national security, and to determine whether these objects represent any advanced technical or scientific information of interest to us." He then went on to describe the Air Force Project Bluebook.

Project Bluebook occupies a single room in a red, windowless building at Wright-Patterson Air Force Base near Dayton, Ohio. It is headed by Major Hector Quintanilla, Jr., USAF. He is assisted by two sergeants and a stenographer, and the office has the responsibility of investigating every UFO reported to the Air Force. In order to help with this formidable task, the Air Force has designated a UFO officer at each one of its United States bases. As the reports come in, it is the responsibility of these officers to begin checking them out.

General Ferguson was asked to summarize the Project Bluebook findings to date. He had the following to say: "Nearly all UFO reports result from observation of natural or conventional objects under unusual conditions. No UFO has ever given any indication of a threat to our national security. Last September we asked the Air Force Scientific Advisory Board to look into our methods for analyzing these reports, to look at the statistics which have been collected, and to make recommendations on what further should be done. The SAB found that UFO's were not a threat to the United States and that the present Air Force program was well organized to investigate them. The SAB also recommended that the Air Force select a few universities to conduct scientific investigations, in depth, into those few UFO reports that warrant such an examination." The SAB is composed of a group of civilian scientists who have achieved considerable eminence in their fields.

Major Quintanilla has also been interviewed by the press. He has done his best to try and clear up some of the misunderstandings about Project Bluebook. "The program is completely unclassified," he has said. "Our files are available to all accredited news media or to anyone working on a book." He went on to say that rumors that the Air Force has a collection of hardware from crashed UFO's are completely false. "We're supposed to have a complete flying saucer in the basement," he noted wryly. "But we don't even have a basement!"

He also said the number of sightings varies with the time of year. "We have very few flying saucers in the wintertime. Whenever a sighting receives national publicity, the number of sightings immediately goes up."

Major Quintanilla has stated that an average of about 1,000 sightings are reported every year. About 2.7 per cent of these cannot be explained by natural phenomena, based on the facts available.

According to the Air Force, most of the flying saucer sightings have a simple and quite rational explanation. Many are the results of seeing the planets, the moon, or bright stars through haze or light cloud layers. There are presently almost 40 earth satellites which are visible to the naked eye, and some of the sightings can be attributed to these. Conventional aircraft and balloons, most of the latter launched from weather stations, cause a large number of UFO reports.

In addition to Project Bluebook, there are two other organizations not associated in any official way with the government which are concerned with flying saucers. The first of these was organized by Major Donald E. Keyhoe, USMC (ret.), and is called the National Investigations Committee on Aerial Phenomena or NICAP. For some years Major Keyhoe has believed that UFO's are visitors from outer space and that the Air Force and the government are trying to cover up the facts.

The second organization is headed by Mr. L. J. Lorenzen of Tucson, Arizona, and has a record of somewhat more objectivity. It is known as the Aerial Phenomena Research Organization (APRO). APRO is dedicated to the proposition that the UFO phenomenon is important enough to warrant objective investigation whether it consists of physical fact or mere rumors. A number of highly reputable scientists and professors are members of APRO.

Are flying saucers in fact visitors from outer space? The best that one can say today is that no completely objective analyst can be absolutely certain that they are not. So far they have mainly been somewhat distant visual phenomena. Some of the relatively few pictures obtained of them are quite remarkable but not conclusive. There have been no verified cases where saucer spacemen have tried to communicate with humans, and no one has been able to produce any flying saucer artifacts which could withstand scientific analysis. From what we know of the laws of physics, the great barrier of distance would appear to make the voyage to earth from outer space forever impossible. But humble creatures that we are, we do not know all there is to know about the laws of physics.

Dr. Hynek has said: "It is easy to dismiss the cases of birds, balloons and the like, but when good solid citizens report something puzzling, I believe we have an obligation to do as good a job as we can. I regard the 'Unidentifieds' as a sort of blot on the escutcheon. Somehow we scientists should be able to come up with answers for these things."

It is hard to make a good case that the government and

the U.S. Air Force are engaged in a vast conspiracy to hide the true facts from the rest of us. In fact it is much easier to make the case that those who engage in such outrageous claims are merely trying to gain publicity and make a profit through a form of modern yellow journalism.

The cooperative program between the Air Force and its group of selected universities appears to be an excellent approach to a truly objective and scientific UFO analysis program. It may provide us with some definite answers to the riddle of flying saucers during the next few years. For the present we can only speculate. Perhaps we will find out soon, perhaps never.

3 | THE MYSTERY OF COMMUNICATION

Man is standing on the threshold of a great adventure—that of searching for other intelligent life beyond the earth. We can be reasonably confident that any intelligent beings we might be able to contact in space have gone through a period of growth and development which is at least somewhat similar to ours.

In the symbolic language of science, which depends on curves and formulae, the progression which has led to our present place on the evolutionary stairway is best described by reference to the *learning curve*. According to those who subscribe to one variation of the learning curve, man's ability to overcome new obstacles proceeds at an ever-accelerating rate. For our learning curve to remain fully consistent with its past shape we must learn more in this decade than in the last, more in this century than in all the past ages.

The human characteristic that biologists consider to have been the most significant in man's achieving success and prosperity on this planet is speech. We usually think of speech in terms of a series of sounds, but this is not the whole story. A monkey cries and a dog barks, but this is not speech, even though the cry and the bark have nuances of meaning.

A deaf and mute human can communicate far better than can dogs and monkeys; for true speech requires the exchange of information. Parakeets can be taught words but not speech.

To speak is to deal in symbols. It is to recall the past and predict the future. Once we had achieved this power of communication, learning to record information followed naturally and swiftly, and we knew not only the present but the sum of the past as well. It was at this precise instant that we became the most formidable of all beasts. No animal which had to start from scratch with each generation could hope to compete with us. And as the past deepened, with all its infinite variations of know-how and meaning, the sum of information for each succeeding generation was multiplied many times.

The power of communication also allowed the development of group action. This is not blind duplication of movement, such as is practiced by herds of cattle and goats, but is somewhat like the organization of ants wherein each individual is assigned specialized tasks which further the group objectives.

These two results of the possession of speech, the capabilities for group action and communication, caused the human learning curve to begin sweeping upward at an ever-accelerating rate.

The desire to communicate is as old as humanity itself. Not only do we seek to share our feelings and experiences with one another, but since the earliest times we have sought to communicate with the future and to learn of the past, as evidenced by the ancient symbols on the early cave walls and by our interest in history.

It would indeed be marvelously interesting to converse with other life forms. Fiction is full of heroes who talked with horses and dogs and even birds. Besides, communicating with other life on the earth could be the forerunner of the even more exciting prospect of communicating with life on other planets.

There are many good reasons for believing that men

and animals might be able to achieve a common language. Scientists have long been aware that there are means of exchanging information which are used by penguins, bats, porpoises, and the great whales. Attempts by humans to communicate with animals have not been very successful to date, however. Some birds, parrots for example, imitate human speech and can make sounds that seem intelligent. But this mimicking of words is not communication. Scientists who had studied the sounds made by these birds have concluded that their talk is like that of a demented man—random and without meaning. Attempts to talk with monkeys, supposedly our nearest relatives on the evolutionary scale, have met with failure, probably because the monkey has been unable to learn human language and reproduce its sounds.

It appears that there are very few animals with the intellectual potential for speech, and these are the ones with the largest brains. Monkeys have a considerably smaller brain than man, and so do birds and fish. The only creatures having brains of comparable weight to that of man are elephants and various members of the whale family. Of all of these, the dolphin, which is an air-breathing small whale and therefore not a fish at all, seems to have the most man-like brain.

Dolphins are called porpoises by most scientists. They are warm-blooded mammals with large cranial cavities, and their brains have a texture which is lined and wrinkled in a way that is unique among the lower animals. Only man has brain tissue of equal complexity.

Sociologists who have observed the social behavior of the bottle-nosed dolphin, both in freedom and captivity, say that their way of life suggests a very high order of mental activity.

As early as World War I, a device called sonar was developed to assist in the detection of enemy submarines. Sonar works by sending pulses of sound energy through the water which return as echoes when they strike the hull of a submarine or some other solid object. Through two wars scientists have been working to improve sonar, and the U.S. Navy has a number of high priority programs for this purpose.

Dolphins possess their own sonar, and the device given

24

to them by nature far outstrips the best that modern science can produce. The sonar noise-maker of the dolphin consists of two trumpet-like formations, one on either side of its nose. These produce a series of clicks which the dolphin uses for ranging. Unlike human sonar, the dolphin uses a wide spectrum of sounds, some of which are audible to us, and others which are many octaves above the upper limits of our hearing. This wide range of sound provides the porpoise with much more knowledge about his watery environment than man is able to glean with his unsatisfactory mechanical sonar. Perhaps one of the most amazing aspects of the dolphin listening instrument is that it weighs only a few pounds. The complete weight of modern human sonar equipment must be measured in tons.

Another characteristic of dolphin sonar is that it is able to fix the direction of objects with extreme accuracy. Scientists feel that this ability is enhanced by the dolphin's flat head. The front portion of his skull is dish-shaped, and this appears to focus the sound he emits in much the same way that the reflector of a flashlight focuses the light rays.

The dolphin appears to carry with him his own stereo receiving equipment. He has ears strategically located on his head to give him the best response from his sonar. Using them, he can tell not only the distance of objects but also their size and shape. Except for color, his ears tell him almost as much about his world as human eyes tell us about ours.

The dolphin lives in a well-organized group which, like General Motors, has a president and a board of directors. As did the early settlers who traveled across the plains, dolphins employ scouts when they are cruising into new territory. If a scout swims back to the herd with interesting news, the board of directors holds a council. Sometimes a new scout is sent out to obtain more information. Ultimately the board makes a decision which is obeyed by all.

Professional animal trainers who have worked with bottle-nosed dolphins are amazed at how quickly they learn and how much they remember. One trainer recently said: "Chimpanzees, dogs, horses and elephants

25

are dull as mice after you've worked with porpoises."

Almost all scientists agree that dolphins are brighter than dogs and cats. A number of them are confident that the dolphin's I.Q. is higher than that of any of the monkeys. A few are now saying somewhat tentatively that on a purely intellectual basis dolphins may even be smarter than man. These scientists must face a number of questions, such as: "How many Cadillacs are driven by dolphins?" and "Since when did a dolphin build a swimming pool for a man?"

These questions are certainly valid. And they demonstrate one thing about dolphin intelligence—namely, it is non-technical. But from this are we safe in deducing that all non-technical intelligence is inferior to intelligence which is devoted to the task of making things? Not necessarily. Man is a product of a different environment, which permits and encourages the growth of a technology. Would man be inclined to build a fire if he were never cold? He has arms and hands to build things with, and he has the vast assortment of materials which is provided for his use by the land. What would he build if he were equipped only with flippers and lived in the sea?

Life tailors itself to a specific environment, and the evolutionary process results in the survival of the best-equipped to meet specific conditions. It would be difficult to prove the argument that all high-order intelligence must concern itself with technology.

These facts raise some fundamental questions facing the scientists involved in the attempt to contact intelligent life on other planets. Suppose most of the intelligent beings in the universe are non-technical, and do not spend time building radio transmitters and receiving equipment?

There are other factors which complicate the problem. Most of the earth is covered with water. Suppose there was no land at all? Would we have developed in such a way as to be building space ships and telescopes? Probably not. But we have dominated the earth most completely with the aid of technology, and no other animal is a match for us. This must lead us toward the conclusion that life which creates a technology of its own has a much greater chance of survival than non-technical life. We know that in an environment similar to that found on the earth, technical life has a tremendous advantage. The odds must be overwhelming that this is also true on a fair percentage of the other planets in the universe which provide an environment capable of supporting life.

The U.S. Government is spending more than $250,000 a year trying to find out more about the bottle-nosed dolphin. The National Aeronautics and Space Administration and the Office of Naval Research have probably invested most heavily in dolphins. The National Science Foundation, the Institute of Health, and the Air Force are also heavy contributors.

Why should anyone, let alone the U.S. Air Force, be interested in talking to a fish?

There are a number of reasons. A talking dolphin could explain to us many baffling mysteries of the sea. It could describe the ways of fish, and perhaps lead us to lost treasures in the murky depths. Dolphins can hear and locate a penny dropped into the water many feet away. No doubt they can also hear submarines, and aircraft which crash at sea, over distances far greater than men can detect them now. Perhaps the most compelling reason of all is that right now we can converse only with ourselves.

Our ability to talk with other creatures than ourselves may first come through communication with non-technical life on the earth. The bottle-nosed dolphin appears to be the best candidate we have been able to find so far. But in order to talk with dolphins we must first discover how they talk to each other.

Languages are divided into two types, called "analog" and "digital." By far the most widely used language is analog. This type utilizes one sound or word to express a complete thought. Suppose I nod my head meaning "Yes, I would like to go to the movies." This would be analog language if that were precisely what I meant each time I nodded my head. However, such is not the case. When I nod I merely mean *yes*, just as I merely mean *no* when I shake my head. My precise

27

meaning at the moment depends entirely on what has gone before and may have nothing at all to do with going to the movies.

In the words of engineers, *yes* and *no* are bits, and each bit can be represented by a digit, hence the term digital language. For example, we could let *yes* be represented by the digit 1, and *no* be represented by the digit 2. To actually express ideas, we combine these bits or digits in many different ways. It is this infinite variety and combination of the bits in the digital vocabulary of our language which gives it color and richness and allows us to express so many shades of meaning.

Dogs, on the other hand, think and speak in analog language. When a dog growls, he is angry. When he howls he is unhappy; and his bark generally means that he is excited. Even his tail plays a part in his language, since he expresses friendship by wagging it. Since each of his utterances expresses a complete thought, his number of combinations and hence his vocabulary is very limited. In human digital language many bits must be joined together in just the right way to form a complete thought, thus allowing more precision and greater variety of expression.

There is no doubt that man's language is one of his greatest advantages. Even a small vocabulary of bits can be joined together in a wide variety of combinations to create a large number of thoughts. The ability to record and pass on the benefits of past experience by means of digital language has probably been the most important single facility which man has developed. Without it each succeeding generation would have to retrace the accomplishments of the past, and our ability to progress would have been severely limited.

Digital languages are much more difficult to learn and interpret than are analog languages. A word such as telescope does not provide us with any hint or picture of what a telescope actually looks like or what it can be used for. However, it is quite easy to interpret the analog purr of a kitten after hearing it once.

A large portion of all language is transmitted by gesture, tone of voice, expression, and inflection. A sociologist has estimated that humans put across almost 80 per cent of their real meaning with these side-effects of conversation. All of us are familiar with the fellow who just can't tell a funny story even though he knows all the words. According to psychologists, personality plays a larger part in our communication process than we realize. Animals that are restricted to analog languages are even more dependent upon gestures and expression to get their point across.

Dolphins are particularly ineffective when it comes to facial expressions because their faces are quite rigid, frozen into a perpetual wooden smile. They also suffer from the disadvantage of having to communicate under water, a far more difficult medium than air.

Some scientists are attempting to learn the language of dolphins; others are attempting to teach them human language. The Lockheed Aircraft Corporation has a project to learn dolphinese, and Lockheed scientists have learned more than 30 dolphin words. Dolphins seem to communicate in a series of very rapid, high-pitched whistling sounds. In addition to whistles, they transmit barks, groans, moans, clicks, grunts, and even quacks.

A group of scientists at the Sperry Gyroscope Company are using a device called the Sceptron to analyze the dolphin communication process. The Sceptron consists of a complex memory circuit which utilizes photoelectric cells. These are used to read out the sounds which are converted to light rays. In order to use the Sceptron, records are first made of dolphin sounds, and these are played into the instrument at somewhat slower than the actual dolphin "talking" speed. The engineers then feed into the Sceptron human sounds which imitate those of the porpoise. The output of the Sceptron indicates the degree of similarity between the human input and the actual dolphin words.

Experiments can also be conducted with the Sceptron to train the dolphin in the use of human sounds. This uses the ability of the device to "memorize" human words. It is then connected to a food dispenser. Each time the dolphin pronounces the human word correctly, he is rewarded with a fresh mackerel. This arrangement can even be made automatic in order that a dolphin can practice by himself without an instructor.

Although attempts to communicate with dolphins have been inconclusive to date, devices like the Sceptron offer a considerable promise that speech with intelligent animals may be possible in the future.

Trying to talk with animals is a new human activity about which we know very little at present. If we can unlock the thought processes of lower animals it will be a major milestone and will teach us a great deal about our world and ourselves. It will also be the first step toward a far more exciting endeavor—that of contacting the life of other worlds.

4 | STAR TALK

The problem of talking with dolphins beside a tropical swimming pool is one thing; conversing with strangers from another world across the vast and heedless winds of space is a fantastically more complex operation.

Communications through the mammoth distances of space will also be quite different from gossiping with our next-door neighbor. For instance, if we were to recognize a coded salutation from the star Procyon tonight and broadcast our own greeting immediately, it would be 11 years before the sound of our voice could reach this nearby neighbor. Before the people of Procyon could congratulate us upon joining the interstellar network, 11 more years must elapse—even if they heard our first broadcast. Thus it would take 22 years just to say "Hello!"

Needless to say, we cannot afford to spend much time in observing the amenities. In any event, the social habits of our new-found acquaintances are likely to be quite different from ours, so we can at least hope that our lack of politeness may be overlooked. Fortunately we will still have a great deal in common with this strange and lonesome neighbor who calls to us across the endless night of space. For one thing, we have both developed radio, and this implies a whole list of common techniques and inventions resting upon a common foundation of scientific knowledge.

Such a being must be able to think in terms of language, most probably digital language. He is aware of the same universal and timeless laws of physics as we are. He knows of the electromagnetic spectrum and theory of Maxwell. Some local Einstein has demonstrated the significance of that inexorable yardstick, the speed of light.

Since we can be confident that he knows all these things and probably much more besides, he is in a small sense enough like us so that we will ultimately be able to talk with him. We can also make certain fairly intelligent guesses about his behavior. This is fortunate, because without them we would have little or no chance at all to make contact.

There are most probably three types of signals which we could logically expect to find radiating from a civilized planet. The normal crowded radio and television networks will no doubt be beaming news, music, advertisements, and millions of other words each day to the local citizens; unless, of course, the inhabitants of the planet have found some way to transmit this sort of thing by a kind of thought transference.

Perhaps luckily for us, this local traffic is like the whispered conversations of man and wife, privileged to be forever secret and unknown. It is too far below the general noise level to be heard by scientists of another planet. In our own case this might be a very happy circumstance. If some of the noise which is inflicted upon us in the name of entertainment were to be heard by a distant scientist, his first instinct would surely be to turn off the set. He would search another portion of the heavens and forever pass us by, feeling certain that the earth was some global Tower of Babel populated only by madmen who had no recognizable culture.

We can also expect that civilizations which are capable

of transmitting to us have already found others with whom they talk on a regular basis. It is possible that we might intercept some of these conversations, but the chances are remote, since they would have to be beamed in exactly the right direction.

The third and more likely group of signals which we might intercept are those which are transmitted for the purpose of making contact with other planets. These would be especially designed to be picked up by the very kind of search we are planning to undertake.

One of the most important decisions we must make before we begin our astral treasure hunt is where to listen. The radio spectrum is a vast grab bag and our receivers are like small hands groping in the darkness. The odds would be prohibitive that we could come up with intelligible signals merely by spinning the dials on our receiver set. This would require that we be on the right frequency at the right time with our antenna pointed in precisely the right direction. For reasons that will be clear later, this is far too much to ask even of Lady Luck.

Fortunately it won't be necessary. There is a signpost in the radio spectrum so clear and unmistakable that it fairly shouts at anyone wishing to contact other life. This is the hydrogen emission frequency of about 1,420 megacycles, a natural frequency at which hydrogen atoms release energy. It contains far more radiated energy than any other portion of the electromagnetic rainbow, and it is here that we must look for our new acquaintance. If he is transmitting at all we will find him nearby, for he has learned to think in the same disciplined way as we, and he will know that the hydrogen emission frequency is known to radio astronomers throughout the cosmos.

We can quite logically make another guess. Our intelligent neighbor will divide his message into two parts. The first will be a sort of call signal used to attract attention. He will decide what signal will most likely be recognized quickly as being of intelligent origin, and will transmit that one. He will also transmit information messages designed to introduce himself to the universe.

If he is a truly altruistic neighbor these latter messages

will contain, besides a description of himself, a rapid brief of his latest and most precious knowledge. He will transmit these without waiting for reply, on the assumption that somewhere in the dim reaches beyond his solar system they will be heard by someone who can make use of them. Because he is intelligent and not too remote from us, he will know our sun has a good chance of supporting life, and for this reason he will broadcast in our direction.

His primary interest will be like ours—to *communicate* with life on other planets. Communication implies a two-way street. He cannot broadcast "at large" like a radio station, because to do so would require huge quantities of energy beyond that which is available to him. To broadcast radio signals in all directions at once requires about the same amount of energy that is used up by the sun in radiant light and heat. By using a directional antenna, much less energy can be used to reach out the same distance.

The requirement to transmit his energy in a narrow, highly directional beam creates one significant problem. There is no way that he can be sure which planets support intelligent life. Indeed, unless he is much more clever than we, he will not even be sure which of the stars in his neighborhood have planets. Like ourselves, he must make some sort of guesses as to which stars are the most profitable objects of investigation.

The best way for him to proceed under these circumstances is to go around knocking on doors, like a Fuller Brush salesman. He will pick a number of stars which his transmitting equipment will reach reasonably well—say, all those within 50 light years. He will discard certain types, such as dark stars, and others which do not radiate much heat and light. He will also avoid double stars, because it is more difficult for the planets of a binary system to maintain a moderate temperature, since their orbits tend to be somewhat erratic. He will then choose the most likely of the remainder and begin his search.

Suppose he were to direct his signals in our direction, how much time could he afford to devote to us before

33

passing on to another planet? The answer to this question is clear as long as we remember that his initial objective is to obtain a response. He should direct his signals towards us just long enough for us to recognize them. Then he must go on to the next prospect on his list. He will surely not waste time and energy sending signals until he gets a reply. This would be so foolish that most of his potential listeners would soon begin to speculate about his sanity.

Moving on after a brief knock at our door is of course optimum from his point of view, not ours. We would be much happier if he would adopt the less profitable gambit of concentrating on us until we had a chance to reply.

This comes back to our analogy of the brush salesman whose basic objective is to talk to several housewives and thereby sell some brushes. He cannot afford to pound on one door all morning. True, the lady of the house may be down in the basement doing the wash. She might hear him only after a persistent knocking. All the same, it is still better for him to knock firmly once and then go on if he does not get an immediate response.

In the case of searching for intelligent neighbors in space, we cannot even afford to wait until someone comes to the door before moving on. After all, it would take more than eight years for citizens of the nearest star, Alpha Centauri, to receive our reply if we were to pick up its first signal.

As a matter of practical fact, an intelligent scientist who is setting out to communicate with other life would probably program his equipment to interrogate several planets per day. He would not come back to them again until he had transmitted to planets which may be orbiting all the most likely stars within range of his equipment, or until sufficient time had elapsed for them to answer him. He would probably beam his signals a little longer toward the faraway stars because it would take longer to distinguish the weaker signals from the background noise.

In light of these facts, we could expect that a planet 10 light years away might support life which would transmit in our direction perhaps only part of one day in

20 years. The odds of receiving signals sent by any one planet on such an infrequent schedule are very small indeed. But there are other factors which make the situation more encouraging.

It would be a great achievement to communicate with life 1,000 light years or more away, but many generations must live and die before two-way contact could be established. Such a remote civilization might fade into oblivion before our first signals reached it. Indeed, we ourselves might be swept away by a new microbe or by an atomic holocaust before the first returning welcome could herald success.

Already we have built radio receiving equipment which can be used to distinguish strong, directional signals at a distance of 15 light years. But the power requirements rise very sharply with distance, and the effort required to communicate with radio over distances of thousands of light years begins to approach the cost of manned space exploration systems.

All we really need to do to gain confidence is to lift our eyes toward the heavens on a clear night. There are 7,000 stars within 100 light years of the earth. Surely, within this myriad profusion there must be a few that are trying to communicate.

We are likely to communicate, at least at first, with life which has proceeded much farther up the evolutionary stairs than ourselves. When we hear the first signals from another world, we will be like boys entering a new school. Those we talk to at first will not be conversing with us to add to their own storehouse of knowledge, for they will most surely know more than we.

It is much easier and more practical to break into the interstellar communications network by listening than by transmitting. Listening is a far less expensive activity, and much less trying from a technical viewpoint. However, listening requires one mature attribute which as yet we have not demonstrated to a marked degree: patience. Whether or not a reluctant and perhaps scientifically unimaginative body of politicians will provide money year after year for such a project in the face of some initial discouragement remains to be seen.

It is interesting to speculate for a moment on what we might expect the first signals to contain. They must be sufficiently striking and unique that our new friends can feel sure we will recognize that they are different from the discordant and random noise of space. At the same time, each precious pulse of energy must be weighed carefully to make sure that every message passes along the maximum amount of useful information.

The words of another civilization will of course be quite meaningless to us at first, but numbers will make sense. A single object is still unity whether it applies to apples or cars or flying saucers.

For example, our acquaintance might transmit the number corresponding to the exact wave length of his transmitting frequency. He could do this by simply allowing a single pulse to equal one, two pulses for two, and so forth. A more useful and reasonable way would be to transmit the same information in a simple binary code which we would learn to decode almost immediately. However, since our units of measurement would not be the same as his, we would not recognize this number as his wave length, and he would probably seek a more universal figure to use in teaching us his numbering system.

Perhaps to get our attention he might transmit some constant which does not depend on units. The figure 3.14, which represents *pi,* the relationship between the diameter and the circumference of a circle, is such a number. Any civilization which has gotten past the early grades in arithmetic would be aware of the universal nature of *pi*. He could rightly expect our scientists to recognize it immediately. From this simple beginning, he would progress to a brief but necessary elementary lesson in his language.

Anyone attempting to contact earth-life will make one very significant assumption regarding us. He will certainly expect us to have the marvelously enhancing capability of sight. While it is true that there have been many wonderful humans with great gifts who were blind, it is hard to visualize a highly advanced civilization based on a sightless citizenry. There is a lot of truth in the old saying, "In the land of the blind, the one-eyed man is king." The hard rules of the evolutionary struggle for survival are such that the faculty of being able to see is an incomparable advantage. In the ultimate, a living organism is no better than its senses, and of these sight is by far the most important.

Sight is also extremely common in life. Shrimp have eyes, and so do birds and bugs, as well as humans. Therefore he is reasonably safe in assuming that we can see, and perhaps the easiest way of communicating with us is to send us a few television pictures about himself. The old adage that one picture is worth a thousand words applies just as well in space as it does on earth.

How will he know we have discovered television? The invention of TV does not lag far behind radio, and he will know this from his own experience. He can be quite confident that a society which is capable of listening to his signals at all will be capable of constructing a television scanning pattern, and that is what he will send us next.

In November, 1961, a meeting was held at the National Radio Astronomy Observatory, Green Bank, West Virginia, to discuss the possibilities of communicating with other worlds. The chairman of the conference was Dr. Frank Drake of the observatory staff. Dr. Drake was the director of Project Ozma, the first brief attempt to listen for intelligent life in space.

After the meeting, Dr. Drake constructed a message which he felt might be similar to one that could be sent by other-world scientists. He mailed his message to members of "The Order of the Dolphin," who were in fact the people who had attended his conference. Almost all of them were able to decipher the message very quickly.

Such messages are quite easy to compose. For example, suppose we receive a signal on a wave length of 20 centimeters from the vicinity of Tau Ceti, about 11 light years away. We notice that these pulses consist of a series of dots and dashes, with the dashes lasting twice as long as the dots. There are 450 of these, and after a pause the sequence is repeated, like some sort of interstellar Morse-code gibberish in a strange tongue. We record all these pulses carefully, the sequence looks something like this:

```
__ _ • • • _ _____ • _ ____
___ • _____ • _____ • __ • ____
__ • _____ • _____ • ___ • ____
__ • _____ • _____ • ___ • _____ • ____
__ • _____ • _____ • ___ • _____ • ____
• _____ • • • • • • • • _____ • _____ •
____ • ___ • __ • ___ • _____ • _____ • • • •
• ___ • _____ • ___ • ___ • _____ • _____ • • •
• _____ • ___ • _____ • _____ • _____ • • •
__ • _____ • _____ • ___ • _____ • ___
__ • _____ • ___ • ___ • ___ • ___ • _____ • ___ • • •
• • ___ • _____ • ___ • _____ • ___ • _____ • ___ •
• _____ • _____ • _ • ___ • • • • • • • • ___
```

The fact that the dashes last twice as long as the dots sooner or later will suggest to some clever television engineer that we arrange the signals in a scanning pattern where one side is twice the other, in other words an array of 15 x 30.

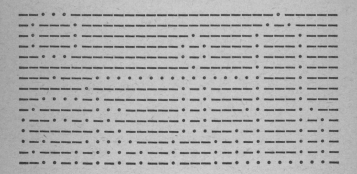

When we drop out the dashes, we have a television picture which looks like this:

Once we establish the scanning pattern, the rest is easy. Our remote communicators are able to tell us a great deal about themselves, even though their message may have taken something less than a second to transmit.

The large crude circle must represent their sun. Five planets are arranged in a line below it. We are actually making the acquaintance of the citizens of two planets in this faraway solar system. Perhaps they have achieved something between worlds that we have so far been unable to effect between nations. Namely, they have joined together in mutual cooperation in the effort to contact other life.

The shorter gentleman makes his home on the third planet—since he is pointing toward it—and he has four legs. Because he is so squat, with such strong underpinning, he may live on a planet which is larger and more dense than the earth.

His taller neighbor lives on the second planet. He has built a space ship in which he journeys to the outermost planet in their solar system, at least the curved line between the second and fifth planet would seem to indicate this. As he has visited this planet, he has probably explored the others also, and this may explain how he met his shorter neighbor. The space ship has a pointed nose and tail fins, which means that it travels through a gaseous atmosphere at some time during its voyages.

The shorter "man" is 6 scans or units high, while the taller is 12. Since the only dimension we have in common is the wave length of 20 centimeters, or about 8 inches, this perhaps means that these "men" are 4 and 8 feet tall respectively. The shorter "man" may have only one arm.

Far better messages than this one can be constructed, providing much more information for the same number of pulses. Instead of using dots and dashes, a more economical method of transmitting would involve the use of dots and blank spaces.

Once contact is established, communication between intelligent beings presents no serious problems. This is true even though they may be permanently separated by billions of cold and empty space miles. We may never meet face to face with these strange and faraway people, but we will still have plenty to talk about, because the mere fact of being intelligent living beings has provided us with much in common. Our communication will most certainly result in great enrichment for us both.

5 | THE INTERSTELLAR DETECTIVES

As we gaze upward at the night sky with its myriads of stars, we peer into a vast mystery. Our earth is situated on the arm of a giant pinwheel about 100,000 light years in diameter and 10,000 light years thick. As the sun sets, a small fraction of the 100 billion stars which our galaxy contains appears before us each clear night.

There are other galaxies—6 billion of them within the range of our largest telescopes—each like a great majestic island floating in the river of space. All are separated by distances so great that they are utterly beyond our comprehension. These vast islands seem to be rushing downstream in a great torrent of energy, some of them proceeding with a velocity of half the speed of light.

Where are the headwaters of the river of space? What is the hurry? Where is this aggregation going so urgently? What is the purpose behind such a gigantic migration of mass and energy? Perhaps most mysterious and intriguing of all: How significant are we—small and weak and humble in this vast and terrifying vortex?

Interest in the stars must be as old as sight. We know that the early humans speculated about the possibility of life amid the glittering profusion of stars which could be seen in ancient times before the development of electric lighting served to hide them from view in many places. After the questions "Who am I?" and "Where did I come from?" must soon have come the equally perplexing ones of "What are the stars?" and "Why do they exist?"

Although these questions have been asked for many generations, logical answers about the construction of the universe have been slow in coming. The first telescopes were directed toward the heavens 350 years ago and they opened many new and exciting vistas. As with most newly invented instruments, the initial gains turned out to be the most spectacular ones.

It was true that the stars were brought nearer, but they were still incredibly far away. Large telescopes were found to be extremely difficult to build and hard to manage. The atmosphere, which appears so remarkably transparent on clear evenings, is actually a dust-filled and opaque window full of distorting currents and shimmering turbulences which limit our ability to solve the stellar mysteries even on the finest nights. It soon became evident that visual astronomy would tell us a great deal that we did not know, but standing alone it would not answer as many of the fundamental questions as we had hoped.

With the invention of radio, a new avenue to the stars was opened, although many years passed before this could be fully appreciated. Perhaps the first scientist to recognize the possibility of listening to radio signals from the stars was Thomas Edison, who conducted an experiment in 1890 to see if he could receive signals from the sun. Professor A. E. Kennelly, an associate of Edison, described the background for this experiment in a letter to an astronomer at Lick Observatory. "Along with the electromagnetic disturbances we receive from the sun, which of course you know we recognize as light and heat, it is not unreasonable to suppose that there will be disturbances on much longer wave lengths. If so, we might translate these into sound . . ." Unfortunately, the sparse records available indicate that the experiment was not successful.

Unlike most scientific developments of this century, the birth of radio astronomy can be established with accuracy, and was primarily the work of one man. Karl Jansky announced his history-making first reception of radio waves from outer space in a professional publication, *Proceedings of the Institute of Radio Engineers,* in December, 1932. The news created a brief sensation. The birth of telescopic astronomy at the hands of Galileo had also caused quite a stir; but unlike this earlier development, the beginning of radio astronomy did not lead immediately to any exciting new finds and the science was allowed to languish until after World War II.

Jansky was working for the Bell Telephone Laboratories when he made his great discovery, and like many another innovator he was actually looking for something else at the time. Bell was attempting to find ways of using radio to transmit telephone messages over a long distance in order to avoid long stretches of expensive phone lines and cables. One of the ideas the laboratory was investigating involved high-powered short-wave transmitters with directional antennas. It was Jansky's job to find out how much of an effect thunderstorms and other natural noise sources might have on such a telephone system.

For this purpose he constructed a rather clumsy contraption which consisted of an antenna mounted on a Ford Model-T rear, turned so that one wheel faced up. On this turned-up portion, Jansky mounted his radio dish. He rotated his antenna around the horizon to determine the direction from which the popping noises of the storms could be heard best.

Jansky soon noticed a most peculiar and puzzling phenomenon. Through a radio loud-speaker, thunderstorms have a sound similar to the snap, crackle, pop of a television serial ad. During certain times of the day Jansky heard only a strange hissing noise very different from what he expected. He found that this sound appeared to come from a certain part of the sky and had nothing to do with thunderstorms. He noted that it traveled across the sky in the same manner as the moon. Being an experienced engineer, he soon arrived at the source of these mysterious radiations. He was actually listening to signals being broadcast from the center of the Milky Way!

Jansky reported his discovery faithfully in the *Proceedings* and it received a modicum of publicity in the United States. A popular radio master of ceremonies of the time even beamed these first strange hissing noises from outer space to his listeners. For a brief time, Jansky found himself in a peculiar position for a radio engineer. He was almost famous. But his notoriety proved to be fleeting. The sounds from the distant stars were interesting as a one-shot news item, but after all they were just noise and the novelty soon wore off. Jansky and his Model-T Ford radio receiver were forgotten—well, almost forgotten.

A man who lived in the small town of Wheaton, Illinois, became interested in Jansky's noise, and as a result of this interest he was the only radio astronomer in the world for several years. His name was Grote Reber and he was an amateur radio buff—not the first and surely not the last amateur to lead the way for the professionals. Reber built the first true radio telescope, a 30-foot-wide parabolic reflector antenna. With it he made some truly remarkable records of cosmic static.

The first interstellar radio noise had been discovered by Jansky on a wave length of 50 feet. Reber was able to get much the same result at wave lengths of 2 feet, where the directional capability of his antenna was much better. He was soon able to map the sky, demonstrating that loud signals came from certain parts of the sky while other sectors were relatively quiet. He was the first to find the startling differences which exist between the visual sky and the radio sky. He was also the first to enter the strange and powerful cosmic world of radio

43

frequency energy which lies beyond the reach of our senses.

Reber could not receive any sounds from objects which could be seen, except for the sun, and he demonstrated that there were giant sources of fantastic power so faint and far away that they will never be seen by human eyes. Amateur though he was, Grote Reber became a true pioneer, and his work formed an excellent first chapter in radio astronomy.

During World War II a number of projects were conducted to evaluate the jamming of Allied radio and radar stations by enemy transmitters. It was soon found that one major source of jamming was not the enemy at all, but the sun. Sun jamming was particularly noticeable during periods of strong sunspot activity. This discovery that sunspots were powerful transmitters of radio energy resulted, after World War II in a great deal of intensive study of the sun, using radio telescopes.

Another result of the early experiments with radar was the discovery of meteor trails. As a meteor passes through the rare upper layers of the atmosphere, it leaves behind a trail of gaseous atoms which have lost some of their electrons—have become ionized, in the words of scientists. These ionization trails show up on radar scopes much as long wires in the sky might appear visually. Radar studies of these trails soon convinced scientists that there were great streams of meteors which flashed through the earth's path almost like schools of fish racing through the sea.

Soon after the end of World War II interest began to increase in radio astronomy. Slowly the realization began to dawn on scientists that there was a radio universe equally as real and significant as the visual universe. Until Jansky's experiments, it had been believed that the brief radiation that could be caught in optical instruments contained the total available information that man could ever hope to glean from the heavens. The new science of radio astronomy effectively doubled the amount of knowledge accessible to man about the universe.

Visual astronomers have long been annoyed by the imperfect window provided by the atmosphere. Light waves are warped and distorted by the atmospheric gases.

They are also impeded or attenuated by the clouds and impurities found in air. These difficulties limit the magnification which can be used in studying the stars, and often make even our nearest neighbors among the planets seem to shiver and shake on the clearest night.

The imperfections of the atmosphere are most apparent through the best telescopes. After 350 years of telescope making we have been able to distinguish features on the moon which are about two city blocks in size. On Mars we can make out objects which are several miles wide, provided that they have considerable length, like the celebrated canals which were first seen by the famous Italian astromer Schiaparelli in 1877 through a 9-inch refractor.

We shall probably never get to the point with earthbound instruments where we can distinguish Martian manmade objects of even such huge size as the Empire State Building. Our atmosphere simply won't permit it. Percival Lowell spent the greater portion of his life attempting to prove the existence of intelligent life on Mars by mapping the canals through one of the finest telescopes ever built. Mainly because of the limitations imposed by the atmosphere, he was unable to convince any substantial number of his scientific colleagues.

If visual telescopes have been limited in the study of possible fellow inhabitants of our solar system, their performance when turned toward the distant stars is even worse. We have never even been able to see a single planet of another sun, although we have other means of demonstrating that they exist which will be described later.

It is far too much to expect that we will be able to see man-made objects on the planets of other suns with telescopes, even though they may have advanced civilizations whose cities cover the whole globe. We will soon have visual observatories outside the earth's atmosphere, and these will be much more useful than our present ones, but even they will not tell us everything we want to know. Vast portions of the sky are blanked out by huge clouds of dark matter which hide all that lies behind them. The center of our own galaxy is hidden forever from us by such a cloud.

Man's position relative to the stars has been likened to

that of the deep-sea fish in relation to the birds which fly over the surface. All that comes to us from them is filtered by the dimming cloak of atmosphere.

Radio astronomy is not without its own transmission problems. And a good many of these are man-made. Just as the city lights have gradually lessened the usefulness of some of the older telescopic observatories, the increased use of electronic signals has complicated the life of the radio astronomer.

Electronic interference is not limited to "line of sight," because radio waves of low frequencies bend around the surface of the earth. At the shorter wave lengths they are reflected back to the earth in unpredictable directions by the upper ionized layers of the atmosphere. This property allows short-wave transmissions to be heard halfway around the world. These short waves cannot be depended upon, however, and the signals tend to fade out just as they are needed most.

Because of these interference problems, radio astronomers locate their stations far away from centers of population, just as the conventional astronomers do. Instead of putting their observatories on top of the highest hills, however, they are more likely to seek out an uninhabited valley surrounded by mountains. A good example is NASA's deep-space tracking station at Goldstone, California, which is located at the edge of a dry lake bed surrounded by hills.

The radio astronomer depends on radiation from the stars, just as the visual astronomer does. Considering that the essential difference between the two types of radiation is one of wave length, it is remarkable that there should be so much difference between the radio universe and the visual one. Radio astronomy suggests that vast quantities of celestial matter is forever destined to be invisible, and cannot be recorded by either our eyes or our optical telescopes. But, using the tools of radio astronomy, a scientist can "see" a cloud of invisible electrons or transparent hydrogen.

One of the earliest discoveries made by Reber was that of a very strong radio signal in the constellation of Cygnus, later designated Cygnus A. Instead of covering several degrees of arc as a nebula does, Cygnus A appears to be a point of energy of incredible power. During World War II, J. S. Hey of the Army Operational Research Group noticed that the output of this gigantic transmitter seemed to fluctuate as though it were sending intelligent signals, except that the fluctations appeared to be random. Scientists soon realized that this apparent pulsing was actually caused by changes in our own ionosphere.

Because of the fantastic power of Cygnus A, efforts were made to determine its exact position, and this was finally accomplished by some astronomers working at Cambridge University in England. The next step was to see if it could be identified visually. After some discussion, Professor Baade of the Mount Wilson Observatory agreed to look for this object with the 200-inch mirror on Mount Palomar, the world's largest telescope.

He found the object almost immediately with a long-exposure camera. Although it is like a great beacon to radio astronomers, Cygnus A is much too faint to be seen by the naked eye, even through a 200-inch telescope. The camera revealed one of the most remarkable photographs ever taken. Baade had taken a picture of what at first appeared to be two huge galaxies in collision. Because of the distance, they appeared like a point to the radio astronomers. This vast clash between two islands of stars, each as large as our own galaxy, seemed to be taking place some 500 million light years from the earth!

Baade discussed his discovery with an astronomer named Minkowski, who was somewhat skeptical of the new find registered faintly on the photographic plates. Baade made a bet with Minkowski that a study of the spectrum of this elusive object would demonstrate that he was correct: that a collision was indeed in progress. The astronomers made a spectrum analysis of the cluster, which appeared to prove that the powerful radio energy transmitted from Cygnus A was being produced by collision. Minkowski duly paid off his wager with a bottle of whisky; an insignificant, perhaps, but at least human, side effect of this far-distant cataclysm.

The materials that compose the nebulae which form Cygnus A are rushing by each other with speeds exceeding a million miles an hour. A very minor part of the energy produced is turned into radio waves, yet this radio energy is equal to the total power output of a whole galaxy of stars like our sun. Even at the incomprehensible distance of 500 million light years, 10 watts of energy reaches the earth from this great beacon.

Since the discovery of Cygnus A, a great many radio galaxies have been found. Some of them are the result of collisions and some are not. Many radio objects have never been identified, since they cannot be seen, even with cameras. Attempts are constantly being made to correlate the radio data with visual information to answer some of the fundamental questions about the universe.

Some of the most intense radiators are not galaxies at all, and among this group is the growing list of objects known at first by the unwieldly name of "quasi-stellar radio sources." This name has lately been shortened to "quasars". They have rapidly become the latest and most spectacular of the heavenly mysteries.

A quasar radio source which burns with a brightness that would eclipse our entire galaxy by a hundred-fold is designated 3C273 in the constellation of Virgo. 3C273 is about 2 billion light years away, one of the most distant objects known. Through a telescope it appears to be a star of about the thirteenth magnitude, and is easily seen through instruments built by amateurs. However, 3C273 is far smaller than a galaxy, despite the powerful radiation it generates. Scientists estimate that it is about 10 light years in diameter, and through a telescope it appears like a giant exclamation point, with a central core and a jet elongation which appears to have been propelled out of it at great speed.

The quasars burn with an intensity of billions of individual stars. They have been described by one astronomer as being "perhaps the most bizarre and puzzling objects ever observed through a telescope." Physicist J. Robert Oppenheimer has called them "spectacular events of unprecedented grandeur, incredibly beautiful." They produce far more energy than any other stellar object, even the collision of galaxies. At the present time they are a deep mystery about which we can only theorize.

Radio telescopes have also been trained on our planetary neighbors. Nothing, unfortunately, has been heard which could compare with our own modern radio programs, bad as we may think these are. In fact, it has generally been hard to distinguish the distinctive sounds of the planets from pure radio noise. The wave length of planetary emissions is proportional to temperature, and in a series of experiments in 1957 tentative measurements were made of the surface temperature of Venus, Mars, and Jupiter, using radio waves.

Venus is covered with dense clouds which have prevented our best visual telescopes from obtaining any information about the Venusian surface features, and generations of scientists conceded that the topography of this planet would probably remain forever a mystery. However the Goldstone, California, radar of the Jet Propulsion Laboratory has determined that the rotation rate of the planet is equal to 243.2 earth days.

Radar has also led to the detection of ice crystals in the Venusian atmosphere, and although the surface temperature of the planet is still subject to considerable debate, there can be little doubt that the equatorial regions are hot enough to bake bread. Some scientists, notably Dr. John Strong of Johns Hopkins University, have theorized that the temperate regions of the planet may provide a suitable life environment. However, Venus would be a rather gloomy place to live, even with air conditioning.

Two radio astronomers, Burke and Franklin, working at the Carnegie Institution in Washington, were experimenting with a new antenna on the low frequency of 20 megacycles. They noted a rather amazing bit of interference which appeared for only a few moments each day on their equipment. This unusual noise did not come from any fixed position in the sky, and for a while Burke and Franklin thought they were dealing with some sort of interference generated on the ground. They searched diligently but the source eluded them.

After some experimentation, they noticed that Jupiter was passing over their antenna at exactly the time of the disturbance. Sure enough, they had received the first signals from our largest neighboring planet. Jupiter radiates on a narrow band of frequencies in the 20-megacycle band, and at first we believed that these signals were generated by gigantic Jovian thunderstorms far worse than any we experience on earth. These radiations were found to be very different from those of lightning, however, and scientists have still not satisfactorily explained them.

6 | THE BIG BOUNCE

All that we know of the outside world comes to us down the broad and many-faceted highway of our senses. Close our eyes and the lights go out. Plug our ears and the music stops.

The same is true for the universe beyond our world. For many generations astronomers believed they could learn no more about the stars than the faint bits of knowledge transmitted to them via the relatively narrow band of frequencies which make up visible light. Radio astronomy has caused a radical change in this belief and has introduced a wide new range of frequencies which can be used to explore and investigate the vast unknown domain beyond this planet.

In all this great spectrum which we are now able to scan with a bewildering variety of instruments, there is one wave length which stands out among all others. This frequency is the unique emission given off by interstellar hydrogen at 1420.4 megacycles. It is a pulse which has become the eternal cry of creation, and it has a primary significance for the interstellar detectives who seek to contact intelligent life on other planets.

During World War II there was little of practical value that could be accomplished at the Leiden Observatory in Holland. The country was occupied early in the war, and most of the more lively young students were carted off to labor camps by the Nazis. It was a difficult time to become really interested in astronomy.

Professor Jan Oort was director of the observatory, and one of his few remaining students was a bright young scientist named Hendrik Van de Hulst. This young man had heard about the new science of radio astronomy and asked his professor to support a program in this field.

Doctor Oort was cool to the idea at first. Radio was a very weak tool, he said, to make the exceedingly delicate measurements of distance, velocity, and temperature which are required for any useful work in astronomy. Before one could hope to accomplish anything with radio frequencies, he would first have to find a yardstick similar to one of those used by the visual astronomers—perhaps something like a well-defined spectral line. Yes, that was it! If Van de Hulst wanted any of the few guilders available for research allotted to radio astronomy, he would first have to isolate a material which radiated on a special frequency. This landmark must be clear and unmistakable, so that it could be the universal reference point for a new science.

Van de Hulst set about his task with enthusiasm. He required no money and no expensive equipment. Paper and pencil were the only tools used in the search that had to be conducted on the basis of pure theory alone. It did not take him long and, like many fundamental scientific discoveries, in retrospect it appears incredibly easy.

It was only natural that Van de Hulst would first consider hydrogen. The most fundamental of all building blocks in the cosmos, hydrogen is the lightest and simplest of all materials. It contains only one electron and one proton, and makes up more than 80 per cent of all the matter in the universe. Van de Hulst knew from his college textbooks that a single hydrogen electron may describe either of two orbits as it rotates around its proton. Sometimes, but very rarely, it changes from one orbit to another, releasing energy as it shifts. In the normal course of events a hydrogen electron drifting freely in space could be expected to change its orbit only after several million years. Such shifts are stimulated by the collision of hydrogen atoms which, for the average atom, occurs in our galaxy about every 50 years.

Despite the rarity of hydrogen-atom collisions, Van de Hulst was able to demonstrate that a great deal of energy was liberated in this fashion because of the vast

51

amount of hydrogen present in the universe. He was also able to show that the energy was liberated on one universal frequency and that it should prove detectable by radio telescopes. He calculated that radio astronomers should search on a frequency of about 1,420,000,000 cycles per second (more commonly known as 1,420 megacycles), which corresponds to a wave length of about 21 centimeters, or 8 inches.

Unfortunately, Van de Hulst did not have a radio telescope available to search the sky for this frequency, and the experimental verification of his theory was initially left to other hands. After World War II, the radio frequency of the hydrogen emission line was measured with great precision and was found to be 1,420,405,000 cycles.

It was left to a research student at Harvard, Harold Ewen, to detect Van de Hulst's noise at exactly the right frequency. This was one of the most interesting and valuable pieces of research ever conducted by two students. They were separated by more than 3,000 miles, spoke different languages, and attended different schools. Ewen used a radio telescope which he built himself and installed on the roof of one of the science buildings at Harvard. The total cost of this investigation that was to unlock many secrets of the universe was under $500.

But the good Doctor Oort said that we must be able to measure temperature, velocity, and distance. What does the hydrogen line tell us about these fundamental values? It has told us, for example, that the temperature of hydrogen near the hot stars is about 11,000 ° C. The temperature of the nomadic hydrogen which drifts in space far from the stars ranges downward to minus 150 ° C. We have learned this from studying the intensity of the hydrogen emission line.

The velocity and distance information comes to us from a property known as doppler. The doppler effect causes the famous "red shift" in the light of stars. It also produces the change in pitch which we hear in a train whistle as the train approaches, passes, and then goes on. Doppler appears to make the frequency, and hence the pitch, of approaching objects higher by adding the speed of movement to the velocity of sound, light, or radio waves. As objects move away, the reverse is true and the speed of movement is subtracted from the frequency of radiation. Thus, a train whistle sounds higher as the train approaches and lower as it departs.

The same phenomenon affects light and radio waves from the stars. A measurement of the doppler frequency shift presents us with the velocity and direction of motion of our star. The distant galaxies appear to be moving more rapidly than the nearer ones, and therefore the doppler also gives us an indication of distance.

The hydrogen emission line has a unique fascination for scientists who are interested in contacting intelligent life on other planets. It is by far the most common frequency in all the universe. If all the interstellar noises were changed to an audible pitch and played together on one stereo phonograph record, the sounds generated by hydrogen atoms would surely drown out all the rest. Like a giant broadcasting station with an antenna rising above the street, hydrogen has established its frequency of 1,420 megacycles as the loudest radio program in town.

In selecting a radio frequency for listening to transmitters located on other worlds, our task would be impossible if we had to search through all possible frequencies. Not only would we have to scan each frequency many times to be sure that we did not miss any faint and faraway voice, but we would also have to train our antenna toward each sector of the sky as we did so. We must use such a "directional" antenna in order to pick up the weak distant signals, and this complicates the problem enormously. Not only must we search in frequency but also in direction.

Certainly, any distant scientist who is advanced enough to build a radio transmitter of the required power will know this as well as we do. He will surely pick a frequency that is familiar to all scientists, wherever they may be. We should do the same with our receiver.

The problem can be compared to that of meeting a friend in London for lunch. Perhaps if the phone connection is bad when we make the appointment, we might wind up without a definite rendezvous, facing a situation

53

like this: You know that your friend will be looking for you somewhere at lunchtime, but you are not sure just where the two of you are to meet.

How do you find him? Where do you look?

Obviously, you cannot investigate every street during lunchhour in a huge, crowded city such as London. Somehow you must reduce the possibilities. You can be sure that your friend is faced with the same problem. Basing your search on what you know of the city and of each other, you are seeking a common solution.

Both of you will be trying to decide where the other will be most likely to look. Some place familiar to both of you, no doubt, and one which is well known as a meeting place. Once you have adopted this line of reasoning, there are only a few possibilities: Piccadilly Circus or Trafalgar Square perhaps.

From the point of view of frequency, in space there is only one Piccadilly Circus, and that is at 1,420 megacycles.

The voice we want to hear belongs to one who knows all about the hydrogen emission line. In fact, he probably learned of it many centuries ago. He will also be very much aware that the vicinity of this guide post is the proper place to communicate across the vast distances of space. Those who are capable of listening intelligently to what he has to say can be expected to have learned this same lesson.

There are many difficult problems which we must solve before we can contact other intelligent civilizations. Fortunately, this key question about the proper frequency meeting place is one of the simplest.

Since World War II, radio astronomy has grown very rapidly. There was only one radio astronomer in the whole world 25 years ago, and he was an amateur. In 1964 there was a meeting of the International Astronomical Union, and hundreds of radio astronomers attended.

Where do they all work, and what do they do? One of the largest and most famous radio telescopes in active use is located at Jodrell Bank, Manchester, England. It is under the direction of Dr. Bernard Lovell, one of the world's outstanding radio astronomers.

Perhaps the most well known radio-astronomy observatory in the United States is the one located at Green Bank, West Virginia. The Green Bank Observatory operates under a unique system whereby a group of universities have joined together to support the installation. Some additional help is provided by the government through the National Science Foundation. Project Ozma, the first attempt to contact intelligent life on other planets, was conducted at Green Bank.

The world's largest radio telescope is 1,000 feet in diameter, but instead of being mounted on the usual platform of movable bearings, it is located in a giant hole carefully scooped out of the earth. It was built by the Defense Department's Advanced Research Projects Agency and cost more than $8,000,000. To make sure that it would be free from radio interference, scientists located this enormous instrument near the small town of Arecibo, Puerto Rico, about 18° north of the equator and far removed from any large cities.

The Arecibo telescope is actually a large, carefully constructed metal net made from chicken wire. Since it rests in a hollow formed by the earth, it cannot be trained on all parts of the sky. The energy collected by the giant dish is directed into "feeds" suspended over the center. As the dish cannot be moved, the position of the feeds is changed to listen to the star talk from different parts of the sky. By this means the telescope can be trained up to 20° north or south of vertical. Since the earth rotates under the stars, all the constellations within a 40° belt are within its range.

In all, the Arecibo dish collects energy from an area of over 18 acres. Because of the errors inherent in the construction of such a huge dish, it will not be very efficient at the short wave lengths (8 inches) which are near the hydrogen emission line. At longer wave lengths —about 2 feet or more—it is a very effective ear, capable of reaching into space far beyond anything else we have at present.

Instead of using large dishes which trap radio energy and focus it on a feed or "collector," why can't we depend on regular antennas to provide us with signals from outer space? Simply because such a conventional antenna does not collect enough energy.

The short waves of radio act in a way similar to light waves. They can best be collected in the same way that a reflecting telescope collects light. Increase the size of the dish (or the mirror, in the case of light) and more energy can be collected.

Telescopic dishes and mirrors must be shaped very carefully. A large radio telescope provides a reflecting surface as large as an acre of ground. In order to receive short-wave radio signals, the surface of such a dish must be perfect to less than one-eighth of a wave length.

The Navy started work on a 600-foot movable dish at Sugar Grove, West Virginia, but work on it had to be discontinued, partly because of financial problems, but also because of the difficulties involved in building such a huge dish within the tolerances required for radio astronomy.

The same is true of radio transmitters. We will not receive radio signals from the normal radio stations of faraway stars. Even dance music from Mars would be too faint to receive if broadcast without a directional antenna. The same sort of dish which is needed to collect and beam the transmitted energy is also required for the receiver.

This again is a matter of power. To broadcast a radio pulse which can be heard at the same distance that the sun can be seen would require an equivalent amount of energy. Unless we can find some direct way of harnessing the solar dynamo to the input section of our transmitters we will have to depend upon directional antennas. Even if we knew how to harness the total of the sun's energy we could hardly afford to do so. After all, what would we do for heat and light?

A very grave problem which threatens the future of radio astronomy as well as the radio search for other life concerns the rapid increase in the use of the radio spectrum. Radio astronomy must share the radio frequencies with many important industries and radio, television, radar, and navigation equipment. Just as the bright lights and smog of the cities have caused the visual astronomers to erect their instruments on isolated mountain tops, so the vast energy which is continually being pumped into the radio frequencies is producing many complications for radio astronomers.

Project West Ford, whereby large numbers of electronic reflectors were placed in orbit to be used as reflectors for world-wide communications, has caused many radio astronomers to protest. Some sort of world-wide frequency planning and control is necessary if we are not to flood the entire spectrum with electronic emissions and thereby make the work of the radio astronomer impossible. And this is probably only one of several disciplines that man must master if he is to survive and progress indefinitely.

Since World War II, man has made many vicarious round trips to his nearest neighbor, the moon. These journeys have been completed in just over two seconds by means of radar. The first radar reflections from the moon were received by a Hungarian scientist by the name of Bay. His equipment was not sufficiently powerful or sensitive enough to permit him to bounce his echoes off the surface of the moon in the conventional fashion of radar, and so he was forced to use some ingenuity.

Visual astronomers had already determined the moon's distance at about 230,000 miles. Since light travels about 186,000 miles per second and the radar waves must make two trips—one there and one back—only simple arithmetic was needed to show that Bay could look for his echoes about 2½ seconds after he sent the initial pulses on their way.

By shooting out pulses several seconds apart and listening at the right time after each pulse, he was able electronically to pile one returning signal on top of another and thus demonstrate that the signals came back exactly on schedule. A much more powerful radar belonging to the U.S. Army was able shortly thereafter to duplicate Bay's results in a more conventional manner.

As soon as radar echoes had been successfully bounced off the moon, scientists turned their attention and their instruments toward the planets. The nearest planet, Venus, is 26 million miles away at its closest approach, which means that a radar beam must be 5 million times more powerful to detect echoes from Venus than from the moon. Even so, the radio observatory at Jodrell Bank and a radar station operated by MIT's Lincoln Laboratory in Massachusetts have succeeded in making the trip to Venus and back by radar. Mars will require radar equipment 75 million times more sensitive than that needed to reach the moon, and the other planets are even more difficult to illuminate by radar. The possibility of being able to detect stars beyond our solar system by radar is extremely remote because of the fantastic power required to do so.

7 | WHERE SHOULD WE LOOK?

Tucked away among the vast profusion of stars which fill the heavens are myriads of planets capable of supporting life. Perhaps on a small fraction of these are intelligent beings who are beaming out pulses of energy into the surrounding darkness saying: "We are here. Talk to us. Be our friends."

If, among the countless planets, we must search each one for signs of intelligence, a formidable task lies ahead. As the great English physicist Arthur Eddington wrote: "We know of the prodigality of Nature. How many acorns are scattered for one that grows into an oak? Need Nature be more careful of her stars than of her acorns?"

As a matter of fact, some of the addresses in space are good ones and some are poor ones, just as in almost any city in the United States. An inspection of the probabilities may serve well to reduce for us the total effort required to find new friends in space.

Stars are not distributed uniformly in space. They are arranged in galaxies like huge, majestic islands floating in the vast and formless void. These galaxies are themselves giant pinwheels of energy rotating at great speed. We live in the solar system of a medium-sized star on one of the arms of such a pinwheel.

It would be senseless for us to search for life anywhere but in our own galaxy. The nearest other stellar metropolis, the great galaxy of Andromeda, is 2.2 million light years away, which means that it would take 4.4 million years just to open the door. The electrical power requirements for such a communication are far beyond anything we can hope to achieve.

We need not be downhearted. Our galaxy contains more than 100 billion stars—enough to keep us busy for a while. Some of these are also quite far away, since the galaxy is about 10,000 light years thick and 100,000 light years across.

Our location in this colossal maze is somewhat unfortunate. We are quite far away from the densely populated center of our galactic city, since we live in the suburbs, about two-thirds of the way from middle to rim. From the standpoint of being able to contact other life, the chances would be increased considerably if we were in a location where the population is greater. Nevertheless, the odds are still overwhelmingly in our favor, as we shall see.

In order to make a meaningful estimate of the possibility of finding congenial neighbors in our vicinity, it is worthwhile to conduct a brief inspection of the local geography. Astronomers find it somewhat easier to examine the form and substance of other galaxies than to survey our own. Like the nearby trees which shut out a view of the whole forest, we are surrounded by the material of our own galaxy and its dark gases shield much of the nearby region from view, including the entire galactic center.

There are many different shapes and sizes of galaxies. Some of them are great spheres, others are quite flat. There are galaxies which are composed almost entirely of stars, and others which contain large clouds of drifting hydrogen.

This latter type of galaxy is usually quite flat and the stars are mixed with the gas in tightly wound spirals which rotate at fantastic speeds about the center. Our own galaxy is such a "spiral nebula."

There are also a number of differences between individual stars in our galaxy which appear to correspond to their stage of development. Some stars are extremely hot, radiating a vast quantity of heat and light, while others are relatively cold—probably too cold to support life-bearing planets. Some of the oldest appear to be composed of light gases, and are known as "halo" stars.

It is extremely difficult to determine the age of our galaxy. Only a few years ago scientists thought it was about 2 billion years old, but recent estimates make it much older—somewhere between 10 and 15 billion years. The solar system is 4.5 billion years old, and this number is quite reliably fixed. It has been established by a remarkably precise measuring stick—the rate of decay of radioactive substances.

From these numbers and the fact that we ourselves have evolved since the creation of the solar system, we might logically guess that intelligent life requires about 3 billion years to germinate and catch hold, once a proper environment for it has been established.

One of the original and most baffling of the scientific mysteries is that which surrounds the development of the solar system. Almost all religions begin with the story of creation. Each ancient mythology dutifully presents its own view of how the world began. Unfortunately, scientists have found the story of the true nature of our earth's beginning to be quite elusive, and the vast majority of the theories advanced to explain the genesis of the solar system have not survived the skeptical examination of modern times any better than have the ancient myths.

Perhaps the first true scientist to develop a theory about the beginning of the world was René Descartes, about the middle of the seventeenth century. As was the fashion in those days, Descartes thought the universe was surrounded in an atmosphere of ether. He felt that in a universe filled with ether, together with some sort of primary matter, eddies and currents would gradually form. The friction produced by these eddies would ultimately break up the primordial material into small particles.

According to Descartes, these broken bits of matter would ultimately find their way to the center of the whirlpools that would form under such conditions. Finally, these collections of celestial junk would grow very large and would become the suns. Some of the larger bits would never reach the center of the whirlpools, and would form satellites. Some of these ideas still have backers among modern scientists.

Most modern theories of planetary evolution fall into one of two categories. They are either "monistic" or "dualistic." Generally speaking, the dualistic theories involve a collision or near-collision between the sun and another star. Modern physical theory would seem to indicate that the products of such a close brush would tend to disperse in space rather than to collect to form the planets.

As a result of these and other points raised, most dualistic theories have now been abandoned. For those scientists who are interested in searching for life on other planets, this situation is most gratifying. Space is so vast and the stars so widely separated that near-collisions in space are very rare. Thus, there would be very few planets on which intelligent life could develop. If the dualistic theories were correct, modern man on the earth might well be unique, alone in all the vast realm of creation.

Most modern theories which seek to explain the genesis of the solar system contend that the planets were once part of the sun and were spun off from the parent body. Many of them are faintly reminiscent of the Biblical theory describing the creating of Eve, using Adam's rib.

Almost all theories attempt to explain one peculiar fact which has perplexed scientists throughout this century. Namely, what has happened to the sun's rotational velocity?

Long ago Sir Isaac Newton proposed that energy could neither be created nor destroyed. With some qualifications proposed by Einstein, his theory has stood the test of time. However, the sun seems to have lost a great deal of rotational velocity, or angular momentum as the scientists call it. At least almost all current theories of creation suggest that it should be spinning much more rapidly than it is at present.

Stars are thought to be formed from stellar nebulae which exist originally as huge, twisting clouds of gaseous material. Most stellar nebulae rotate at constant rates. However, as the gases are pulled in by gravitational attraction toward the center, one would expect the rotational speed of the system to increase, in the way that a figure skater begins to spin faster as the arms are brought closer to the body.

This is not the case with our sun. It rotates quite slowly, even though its gaseous arms have all been pulled in to form a solid spherical mass. About 90 per cent of its angular momentum must have been dissipated if the sun was formed from the same sort of stellar nebula that inhabits our universe.

Where did all this rotational velocity go? If Newton was right, it couldn't have just disappeared or swallowed itself up in some kind of celestial Indian rope trick.

A growing number of scientists feel that it was deposited with the planets. This idea gains considerable substance from the fact that if we add up all the angular momentum of the planets, the asteroids, and the sun itself, we come up with a figure which is pretty close to what it should be if the hypothesis is correct. Numerous theories have been advanced to explain how the planets and asteroids broke away from their parent sun.

Some stars appear to have much more rotational velocity than others. This fact gives us an idea of how to begin looking for planets which are likely to have people on them with whom we can talk. We should look for stars which have a low figure of angular momentum. If our theory is correct, such stars may very likely have an interesting family of planets in orbit around them.

Until this point is reached, the temperature of the star has been continually rising. The surrounding planets were cold at first and then were warmed by the increased radiation from their sun. So far the environment of the planets has been far too unstable for the development of life as we know it. The type of life found on our earth is incredibly delicate, almost of a jelly-like texture, and is capable of existing only within extremely narrow physical limits.

Once the thermonuclear reaction stage is reached, the star commences a long period of relative stability. The energy of radiation is precisely balanced by the output of the nuclear reaction. This condition lasts until the hydrogen in the core is exhausted.

Scientists call a star whose radiation is produced by

thermonuclear reaction a "main sequence" star. Once the hydrogen has burned away, the star once again enters a phase where the radiated energy appears to change quite rapidly.

In order for a star to support the development of intelligent life over a period of three billion years it must be a main sequence star: one which has passed through the first growing pains of youth but has not yet reached old age. Some main sequence stars are only in this stage of their development for 10 million years. Others remain on the main sequence for over 100 billion years.

There is another characteristic of a star which has a great deal to do with the probability of finding life on its planets. The solar system was formed 4.5 billion years ago and the first rocks are about 3.5 billion years old. Therefore the first billion years in the development of our earthly home have gone unrecorded.

Nevertheless it has taken over 3 billion years of germination, evolution and development to bring us to our present position where we are just beginning to conjecture on the possibility of life on other planets. Therefore, if our own experience is any guide, a star must provide a stable environment for its planets for a period at least this long in order to produce life we can converse with—unless of course we are unusually backward, in which case this development time might be somewhat reduced.

All cosmologists agree that stars begin as large clouds of gaseous material, mainly hydrogen. The mutual gravitational attraction between particles gradually causes these clouds to contract until they become sharp, hot, gemlike points in the sky. The heat and light generated by a star is maintained either by gravitational attraction or by the thermonuclear reaction of its materials.

In the very beginning, a star is not hot enough to trigger a thermonuclear reaction and the heat is generated purely by the friction of gravity. As the temperature rises, due to the compression of the internal gases, the thermonuclear reaction begins which changes hydrogen into helium in the core of the star.

We have estimated that human existence of the earth is a result of 3 billion years of development. But perhaps we are slow students in the school of life, dullards who deserve to be put near the foot of the class. Is it not possible that life on other planets may have come along much more rapidly, and that we are latecomers to the community of the intelligent?

It is, of course, impossible to answer questions such as these in concrete terms. We have only one example to go by, and this is our own. However, we can postulate that conditions in the vicinity of many stars in our galaxy are similar to those of our own planet. In any event, faster development of intelligent life on other worlds would have the net effect of providing more potential neighbors in space with whom we can communicate. We would be happy if such were the case.

Life appears to develop as a result of a long and difficult evolutionary process. And like all trial-and-error processes, the natural selection of the species is a slow and ponderous one. We must admit in all due modesty, however, that it is incredibly efficient. After all, it produced us!

A great many changes or mutations in life forms are introduced as a result of the bombardment of genes by the various cosmic particles. Perhaps faster mutations might take place on worlds which are more heavily saturated by cosmic or ultraviolet rays. Even so, it is doubtful if this would result in a more efficient and rapid evolutionary process. Most mutations are bad, and actually result in changes for the worse. It is only after they have withstood the environment for a considerable period that they can be truly judged by the process of selection. Through the process of the survival of the fittest, bad mutations perish and only the good live on, to be changed for the better (or worse) again. Faster mutations might even cause life to perish, and it would appear that evolution must proceed at a stable and rather slow rate if it is to result in such remarkable creatures as ourselves.

All the problems will not be solved even when we find a star whose angular momentum suggests it may have a suitable family of planets. This will be true even though the star may be in that part of its life cycle which provides a stable environment, like the protective covering of the greenhouse, to nurture the sort of life we are familiar with.

There is also a certain maximum and minimum distance which a planet must maintain from its sun if it is to receive the necessary amount of light and heat to support life. This zone, within which life can exist, has been called the habitability zone of a star. The habitability zone probably coincides approximately with those limits at which water begins to boil on the one hand when exposed to the sun's heat, and at which it freezes at the other extreme because of the cold.

The size of the habitability zones around stars depends entirely on the amount of energy which they radiate. Large stars, because they are so hot, have a wide zone around them within which life-bearing planets might orbit. Small stars have small habitability zones because they produce less energy.

The possibility of finding life in the vicinity of a small star is decreased by the fact that planetary orbits are usually not circular. This increases the chance that some portion of the orbit may fall outside a narrow habitability zone. When this happens the planet is destined to be like our moon—forever a dead cinder.

About half of the stars in our stellar neighborhood are actually not single stars at all, but are binary or multiple-star systems. Often what appears to the naked eye as a single star turns out, when viewed through a powerful telescope, to be two or more stars revolving around each other. The nearest star, Alpha Centauri, is such a system, containing not two, but three members.

Most astronomers feel that the possibility of finding life in the vicinity of such a group of stars is quite remote. For many such multiple star systems, there is probably no stable orbit which a planet could maintain that would always be within a moderate temperature zone. This is due to the changes which will be produced by each component star on the nearby planetary orbits. In addition, the amount of radiation which a planet would receive from such a system would vary widely as the suns revolved around one another. Sooner or later the summer would become too hot or the cold too severe, and the delicate, faint murmur of life would be stilled forever.

After taking all these factors into account, we might expect that no more than one-fifth of all stars are capable of supporting life. In our own galaxy this limits the number of life-supporting stars to about 20 billion—still enough to make a search program worthwhile.

In our immediate neighborhood there are perhaps three stars which might be expected to support life: our sun, Epsilon Eridani, and Tau Ceti. Epsilon Eridani is 10.8 light years away, and Tau Ceti 11.8. Since the sun has a luminosity three times as great as either of the other two, it has by far the best chance. As a matter of fact, two of the sun's planets—Mars and Earth—lie within its habitability zone.

Although we can speculate that there are many suns in the universe with life-bearing planets in orbit around them, the only planets we have actually seen are those of our own sun. We know that a number of stars, Sirius for example, have darker companions which keep them company on the long voyage through space. But such companion stars are hardly fit for habitation. The dwarf star which accompanies Sirius is so dense that scientists have estimated that one tablespoonful of water on the surface of this body would weigh a ton! Not a very practical place to live.

It would be most helpful if we had some way of detecting the planets around other stars and thus further reducing the number of stars which we must investigate in the quest for other intelligent life. What are the possibilities for doing this?

Unfortunately this is one of the most difficult problems in astronomy. Professor Otto Struve has made a study of the various conceivable techniques, and his conclusions are not optimistic. He found that we could not possibly hope to see a planet even as large as Jupiter through our best telescopes at the distance of the nearest star.

It might be just possible to detect, under precisely the right conditions, a planet the size of Jupiter by means of a device called a photometer. A photometer is an instrument which measures very small changes in light intensity. If such a device was trained on a star at the precise moment some faraway Jupiter passed across its face, then the photometer would measure the difference in intensity of the star's light caused by the eclipse. It would take a great deal of luck and persistence to make such a discovery, since the eclipse would last only a few hours and would occur about once every ten years.

Although we cannot be sure of the existence of planets, we do know that a significant proportion of the stars have lost a major portion of their angular momentum. In addition, half the stars in our vicinity have one or more companion stars. Some of these are quite small. For example, the unseen companion of 61 Cygni is only about one one-hundredth of the size of the primary star. This value is almost halfway between that of stars and of large planets.

There are other characteristics of a life-supporting planet. It must be large enough to capture and hold an atmosphere, but not too large. The hydrogen in its atmosphere must have been at least partially dissipated, because hydrogen does not favor the development of a superior form of life. Large planets tend to retain their hydrogen atmospheres because of the stronger pull of gravity. The secondary atmospheric gases, such as oxygen and carbon dioxide, are necessary for the support of life and these gases must be retained.

Liquid is the great lubricant of the wheel of life, and a habitable planet must have surface water, or at least must provide a fluid of some sort. It is very difficult to imagine the proliferation of highly developed life without the support of liquid.

On the other hand, intelligent technical life would probably have a difficult time in gaining a foothold in a purely liquid environment. Many chemical reactions such as fire do not work well in liquids; and a fluid medium provides a soft, bland, protective coating that presents few of the challenges which seem to be necessary for the development of advanced technical life forms. Fish have remained fish throughout the centuries. It was the creatures who crawled up on the land and faced its dangers and difficulties who developed into man.

8 | ARE WE UNIQUE?

We humans are indeed a magnificent race, unique in the small corner of the universe which we can comprehend. And we are justly proud of our complete and lonely triumph over the terrible adversities which beset our early past. Of all the man-apes who roamed the primeval forests before the last ice age, we alone survive. Of all the species who have come and gone, we alone have an appreciation for beauty and the faculty of wonder. We alone build ships and space capsules. We are the true monarchs of earth, and we carry the torch for more than we know.

Despite all these vast accomplishments, we are incredibly fragile, and our existence is totally dependent on the maintenance of a number of delicate natural balances. A minor mutation in an unknown microbe, a small shift in the chemical constituency of the air, an eruption on the sun—any of these and thousands of other minor perturbations might sweep the human world away.

If this is true, how can one say that the odds are greatly in favor of intelligent beings on other planets? In order to understand the possibilities for other life in the universe, it is worthwhile to take a brief look at the evolution of man in his earthly home and the strange partnership which he has formed with his environment.

Any discussion of evolution must begin with the atmosphere, for air is to us as water is to fish. The ocean surface is the roof of the shark's world, and the lowest atmospheric layer, the troposphere, is man's ceiling. Going out farther requires that man take with him a bubble of the atmospheric temperature, pressure, and elements within which he is mortally bound.

This aerial ocean, under which life has moved for thousands of centuries, is indispensable to all living things. The other planets which orbit our sun are not enfolded in a gaseous envelope of the same ingredients; thus their life, if it exists at all, is not like ours. The moon has no significant atmosphere and is a dead cinder.

But the supply of life-giving elements in our atmosphere, large though it may be, is not unlimited. Each day it is drained and absorbed by the rocks, the soil, the oceans, and all living things. Much of it is forever lost to us, boiled away into outer space. Left unrenewed, the present store of atmospheric carbon dioxide would be completely exhausted in less than 10 years, the oxygen in 3,000 years, and the nitrogen in 100 million years—a mere cosmic instant.

Yet our atmosphere neither changes nor diminishes. Its composition today is essentially the same as that which existed in Cambrian times, half a billion years ago. Why? The answer can be found in the unique relationship between life and the air.

During the long dark ages which led to the evolution of human life on our planet, this mutually beneficial partnership gradually developed. It began in the early dawn of our planet as the atmosphere was born. Most living organisms are so constituted that they depend upon this partnership and contribute to it. Man is no exception.

When we initially became aware of the evolutionary process, we presumed that the sea had mothered the first life. This assumption developed naturally, since most living things are composed largely of liquid. The blood of man exhibits many characteristics of sea water; it is salty and contains the same elements. Furthermore, the oceans offer a soft, protective medium with an even temperature very suitable for the first viscous growth. Today, however, it can be shown that life probably originated, not in the sea of water, but in the sea of air.

Biologists generally agree that the first life existed as a complex protein molecule with one unusual attribute which made it different from all that had come and gone before. It could absorb other molecules and reproduce itself from their materials. Such organic chemicals possessed the two basic requisites of life: they grew and they reproduced themselves.

The building blocks from which complex protein molecules evolve are the amino acids. For some years, scientists suspected that these could be made in the laboratory by duplicating conditions similar to those found in the earth's first primitive atmosphere. Dr. Harold Urey and his associates conducted an experiment to explore this theory. They constructed a test-tube earth with the same characteristics which existed on our planet millions of years ago when life began. The atmosphere in their test tube was composed of methane, ammonia, and hydrogen. Water which contained the same minerals as the primitive oceans was placed in the tube. Then the system was sealed and the water heated until a vapor, resembling that of the ancient clouds, formed. Small electrodes energized the circulating gases, producing a bombardment very similar to that of the powerful radiation beamed forth by the immature sun.

The system was allowed to steam its prehistoric brew for a week. Then it was disconnected and the contents were analyzed. Definite amounts of three amino acids were found, proving that these complex substances which exist in living tissue could have been created in the earth's original atmosphere by chemical reaction.

Dr. Urey and his associates do not claim to have created life in their test-tube earth, nor do they entirely understand the process by which the evolution of organic matter took place. However, their findings do indicate such processes could exist. Had it been possible to provide in the test tube all the probabilities of the vast ocean of air, and were it practical to maintain the system for a long period, they might have seen a replica of the first life-molecule begin to creep up the evolutionary stairs.

It is very possible that these life-molecules were thus appropriately born in the clouds above the planet, spawned in the turbulence of the lightning and the wind. Later they were rained upon the earth and, like all things, ultimately washed into the sea. Once within that mother bosom, they grew and evolved and multiplied until the oceans were teeming with them and life was firmly anchored upon our globe. The sea life grew to invade the land, and from this molecular beginning countless life forms took shape. Yet all were bound by one common denominator—the atmosphere which nourished them.

The first bacteria acted upon the methane, converting it miraculously into carbon dioxide. The green, translucent algae covered the seas with a thin, persistent scum and released oxygen by the mysterious process of photosynthesis. Shortly—as time is measured in the growth of planets—the oxygen-consuming creatures appeared and breathed forth carbon dioxide. The great symbiotic partnership began to replenish the air.

Ultimately, three chemical cycles for the use and renewal of atmospheric elements became established. The carbon dioxide-oxygen cycle, the nitrogen cycle, and the water cycle are the processes by which mankind and the other life forms link soil to atmosphere and preserve the earth's delicate aerial balance. Millions of years ago their operation became fixed and automatic.

The most universal of the chemical cycles is that of carbon dioxide and oxygen, since it involves the participation of every living thing. Oxygen combines with carbon to form two basic gases. One of these is carbon monoxide, which is poisonous. A concentration of four-tenths of one per cent will cause the death of human beings in less than 30 minutes. Differing from this killer only by a single oxygen atom per molecule is carbon dioxide, which is found in great abundance in our atmosphere. It is also present in the soil, in living things, and in the sea. Animals continuously exhale carbon dioxide, which is utilized by the plants, which in turn separate the carbon and return the oxygen to the air—a simple process, but a vital one. Interrupt the cycle, or change its precarious balance, and life would swiftly vanish from our globe.

The sea creatures are not exempt from this chemical Ferris wheel. The oceans of the earth absorb oxygen and carbon dioxide directly from the air. Moreover, the erosion of the beaches yields sediments heavy with carbon dioxide, which are washed into the seas to reinforce the supply provided by the air and the marine life. Fish inhale oxygen, and marine plants require carbon dioxide. The life processes within the oceans are so active that they have become vast reservoirs of carbon dioxide, holding an amount in solution equal to fifty times that suspended in the realm of air.

The chemical conversions of the carbon dioxide-oxygen cycle are quite simple to produce in our laboratories. The reduction of carbon dioxide into its component elements is readily performed by any skilled chemist. Its creation is even easier. Carbon dioxide is a product of combustion and may be generated by merely building a fire. But simple as these actions are in the laboratory, man has yet to discover how living creatures accomplish the magic within their bodies.

Although we think of ourselves as oxygen-breathing creatures, we are more accurately nitrogen-breathing, for this element is by far the most abundant in the canopy of air. Nitrogen composes 78 per cent of the atmospheric gases. It is equally plentiful in the earth's crust, being found wherever there is life. All fertile soils contain it, as do food-stuffs, silk, wool, feathers, and coal. However, the nitrogen in the earth is never found free, as it is in the air, but is always combined with other chemicals.

Still another great cycle wheels along its endless route over our heads. It replenishes a unique and highly stable chemical required by all forms of life. This is the miracle blending of the two gases, hydrogen and oxygen, which we recognize as water.

Water is the lubricant which greases the efficient machinery of all life processes. If its distribution were interrupted, the mechanism would come to a sudden and disastrous halt. Deprived of water's solvent powers, and its ability to transmit food and heat, neither plants nor animals could survive. Even if the surface water were to remain untouched, the absence of water vapor in our atmosphere would release the previously trapped solar rays to escape into space, and our planet would chill to sub-polar cold.

Since man had all the evidence before him, it was most surprising that he failed to understand the water wheel of the sky until recent centuries. Aristotle believed that rainfall united with water emerging from the deep bowels of the earth to form the rivers. The great Plato disagreed. He thought that ocean water flowed through subterranean channels underneath the continents, bubbling forth as springs which replenished the rivers. Centuries later, the Renaissance scientists Kepler and Descartes still subscribed to a modified form of Plato's theory. Earlier, Leonardo da Vinci had suggested that the rivers were created by the run-off of rainfall from the high places of the earth. But two centuries passed before three French scientists proved conclusively that the return of water to the land is the result of the water-carrying capacity of the atmosphere.

As a result, we now understand the functioning of the hydrological cycle better than that of any other. Millions of tons of moisture are absorbed into the atmosphere each day by the process of evaporation. This water returns as rain and snow. It seeps through the earth, forming the rivers which flow into the oceans. One three-thousandth of the earth's total water content is always involved in this moisture transfer. This is enough to submerge the North American continent under a 7-foot layer.

The symbiotic relationship between life and atmosphere extends to the innermost life processes. If all the constituents of air are broken down into their component elements, we find that they bear a remarkable relationship to the chemistry of living things.

The primary atmospheric elements are nitrogen, hydrogen, oxygen, and carbon. These exist in either combined or uncombined form. Analysis of life substances shows that the great majority of living cells are also made up of these four elements. Carbohydrates, vital to life, consist almost entirely of carbon, hydrogen, and oxygen, while proteins are built of these three plus nitrogen. Nitrogen, by far the most abundant atmospheric gas, plays a correspondingly important role in life. It is present in the nucleus of every living cell. In a chemical sense, we can almost say that our human bodies are built of air, so closely is their structure related to the atmospheric elements.

The great partnership between life and the air, which has nourished us since our dim beginnings, has also proved to be our prison as we seek to move outward into space. Engineers must duplicate the intricate and delicate chemical balance of the atmospheric envelope

73

in the hulls of their space ships and on other worlds if our astronauts are to explore the cosmos.

Breaking away from the realm of air to the realm of space will also take us into a new and terrifying energy environment. The highest earth-recorded temperature of 58° C. was registered near Tripoli, while a low of minus 88° C. was recorded recently by Russian scientists near the South Pole. This is a total shift of only 146° C. over the total surface of our earth, and while it is more than enough to roast or freeze our fragile bodies, it is a trifling amount as temperature ranges go in space. The moon, for example, averages about 95 °C. on the side facing the sun, and minus 130 °C. on the dark side.

This matter of temperature control is one of the main items which determines the habitability of other planets. In order to provide a first-class abode for life as we are familiar with it, a planet must have a range of temperatures between the boiling and freezing points of water. This is tantamount to carefully controlled air-conditioning in cosmic terms.

Since time immemorial, our tender body cells have been protected by the atmospheric blanket from the sun's direct rays. Much of this energy, including the burning ultraviolet and fierce cosmic radiation, never reaches the earth's surface because of the filtering effect of the blanket of air. Although we know little about the mass effects of this radiation, what we do know is enough to make us certain that man must be protected from it just as from the terrible heat and cold.

Scientists have postulated that radiation particles which strike the molecules that form the life-shaping genes of living things actually produce mutations in the life forms themselves. Indeed, this is one of the worries regarding the radiation fallout from our atomic tests. However, it is the mutations or changes in living beings which actually produce the variations that are so necessary in the process of evolution. Then isn't it only reasonable for us to expect that some increase in radiation would speed up the evolution of life?

The answer is probably no. Although such a system would indeed produce many variations, most of these would be less efficient than the parent life form. It is

74

unfortunately true that most mutations are poor ones, and operate to the disadvantage of the organism affected. The few good mutations must be changed and shaped many times before they become radical improvements. Such improvement and shaping are painful processes involving a great deal of trial and error. By their very nature they are time-consuming. Errors in copying the subtle differences between parent and child have produced most of the changes which have pulled us up the evolutionary ladder.

Another mysterious terror which faces those who venture outside the atmosphere is that of the cosmic refuse which hurtles through the void at fantastic velocities. We move about upon the earth without fear of meteors because of the sheltering air. Almost all meteoric material is consumed by friction long before it is within range of our senses; the moon has no atmosphere and its pock-marked surface bears ample evidence that an unprotected sphere would be a difficult place on which to live.

The chances of survival for space ships, however, are still quite good. Meteors are distributed over a vast area, within which the most ambitious space ship will be a minute target. Fortunately, large meteors—those bigger than a basketball—are very rare. A grain of cosmic dust large enough to be barely visible might strike an unprotected man on the average of once a year in space, and there is a progressively decreasing probability of larger objects hitting the rocket ship.

There are great areas in space which contain many bits of cosmic garbage; perhaps these are the residue from long-forgotten catastrophes. Space travelers must avoid them, just as the ancient mariners learned to skirt the Sargasso Sea whose seaweed fouled the bottoms of their ships.

The atmospheric canopy shackles us with other "protective" features. The blind deep-sea fish appear to collapse and melt away when removed from within the ocean's pressure, and we of the earth's surface have flesh and bones which are bonded together by the weight of atmosphere. Above 60,000 feet the air pressure becomes so low that liquids boil at the normal temperature of human blood, and the spaceman's body fluids will vaporize almost instantly, tearing his tissues apart and causing him to inflate like a football.

But death comes quickly though less spectacularly from lack of pressure at much lower levels. At 25,000 feet, man has a *useful consciousness* of 3 to 4 minutes if pressurized air is not fed to him directly. At 30,000 feet, his useful consciousness has become one minute, and at 50,000 feet he remains conscious only 15 seconds.

The reason for man's swift demise at 50,000 feet is a graphic illustration of our dependence upon atmospheric weight. At this height, the outside air pressure has fallen to the exhaled pressure inside our lungs. The diaphragm acts as a bellows to produce this low pressure and draw air back into the lungs. No air can be drawn in at the very low pressure existing at 50,000 feet, and therefore there is no way that a man can breathe. He becomes a fish out of water. He gasps futilely as his lungs exhaust the air in them and can obtain no more. Within a few seconds the oxygen stored in his brain tissues is reduced to the point where consciousness is lost. Death follows swiftly.

The biological equivalent of outer space is sometimes taken to be 100,000 feet. At this altitude, man must be protected from the lack of atmospheric pressure, isolated from the outside temperature, provided with atmospheric oxygen to breathe, and shielded from the cosmic rays and direct sunlight.

Man is an earth creature. Although he may roam to the outermost limits of the solar system and beyond, the heritage of the earth will cling to him always. However, if he can break the shackles which chain him to this globe, he surely will be irrevocably changed. Historically, each new environment has produced new creatures, better adapted to the changed conditions than were their predecessors. As he proceeds outward into space, man as we know him today may become a period piece in the furniture of life.

Buried in the unexplored depths of intergalactic space there are millions of planets like our own. Not too hot and not too cold. Small enough so that the crush of gravity has not become an impossible burden, yet large enough to have captured an atmosphere of the heavier gases.

Each of them is an island, isolated by the cold, forbidding vastness of the cosmos. Each of them is rushing in the night through a forlorn and desolate sky, like a transatlantic jet containing a small corner of light and well being—perhaps even the warmth of intelligent companionship.

How many life-bearing planets are there? We can never know the exact number, but statistically we can at least guess that in our own galaxy there should be more than 100,000. Similar to the great airliners which pass blinking in the night, do they carry passengers like us? This is the great enigma whose answer we hope to seek out before the end of this century.

One can make a convincing argument that somewhere in this huge grab bag there are creatures very much like ourselves. Nature, just like the automobile designers in Detroit, appears to use a good idea more than once. Oak trees and rose bushes have many similarities in the way that their roots collect food from the earth, their sap flows, and their leaves use the energy of the sun in the food-conversion process. Other plants are much the same.

Among the more complex animals, the similarities are even more striking. Men have eyes and ears, and so do camels, reindeer, and squirrels. The close parallels between the evolutionary steps and the ultimate results among the earth's creatures suggests that many functional characteristics are almost fixed as soon as life begins to germinate from a given set of chemicals. The brains,

77

livers, stomachs, and hearts of most mammals are sufficiently similar so that biologists feel the growth of many of these organs is inevitable in the evolutionary process, at least for life born in a carbon, water, and oxygen environment.

From our studies based on that marvelous instrument, the spectroscope, we know that the stars contain the same elements as our sun. Since these fundamental particles are the basic building blocks of the universe, we can expect that most planets have a chemical composition somewhat like our own. Many of these planets are probably of similar weight and size. As a result, they have no doubt captured a similar atmosphere and exert a comparable pull of gravity.

The same combination of the natural elements will always produce the same end products. This scientific fact is well known to chemists and astronomers alike. It has been expressed very neatly by Dr. Harlow Shapley in his extremely interesting book *Of Stars and Men.* "A mixture of pure chemical elements will always under the same physical conditions produce the same result, whether it be an odor, an explosion, or a color. Perhaps we should expect that a mixture of starshine, water, carbon, nitrogen, and other atoms, when physical conditions are fairly similar, will everywhere produce animals that are much alike in structure and operation and plants that have certain standard behavior, notwithstanding great morphological differences. If we should visit a planet essentially identical with ours in mass, temperature, age, and structure, we would probably not find the biology queer beyond comprehension. We might find it no more peculiar than we would find the biology if we were transported on our own planet into Carboniferous times, or taken back just 150,000,000 years when the great lizards ruled the land and sea, and the birds, mammals, and flowering plants were not yet far developed.

"Therefore we surmise that the biology on Planet X and Planets Y, Z, and so forth, might have much in common with the living forms on Planet Earth just because the carbon compounds will have it so, and because the same chemistry and the same natural laws prevail throughout the universe we explore."

Since the basic laws of chemistry and physics appear to be universal and timeless, it is not too much to expect that similar environments should produce similar children. All indications in our own world would appear to point in this direction.

Not only can we expect that the people of other planets might resemble us physically, but they may have social characteristics somewhat like our own. Ants, for example, have a group structure quite like that of bees. Both societies have queens at the top of the social pyramid and workers at the bottom. There are many such parallels between men and animals; even the social characteristics of insects carry over into human society. Biologists have long been amazed that animals with vastly different appearances and physical characteristics nevertheless have comparable growth and social patterns.

It would appear that all animals which band together in groups must adopt some sort of organization to advance the general good if they are to survive. This principle is no doubt of universal application, and the right type of organization for men may be quite like that most useful for the citizens of many other planets. In fact, we might be fortunate enough to contact a society with sufficient wisdom and intelligence to advise us how we might increase the stability of our own somewhat precarious world situation!

In addition, and this is most important from the standpoint of communication, we can expect highly developed forms of life to have similar sensory organs. The gases of the atmosphere are excellent carriers of sound waves, provided they are required to travel only short distances. Even atmospheres of different characteristics from our own will carry human speech. Helium has been substituted for nitrogen in the atmosphere of pressure chambers, for example, and human voices could still be understood, although they were several octaves higher than normal.

The higher frequencies, such as those of light, are also universally available to be intercepted and interpreted by properly constructed eyes. We can expect that intelligent and capable life on other planets will surely be able to make use of the information which is available on these wave lengths. Life, however intelligent it might be, would face tremendous odds in advancing to the point where it could build radio and television sets without a full set of sensory equipment at least as fully developed as ours.

In fact, highly developed life forms may even possess senses which we do not have. Compared to the top-drawer candidates from some of the more highly developed planets, we may be like the color-blind bull, attracted by the matador's cape merely because it moves.

There are many indications that our sensory organs detect only a small fraction of all that is available for detection. Over a period of years, a group of scientists headed by Dr. J. B. Rhine of Duke University have conducted experiments in extrasensory perception (ESP).

The standard Duke University experiment involves two persons in separate rooms. One subject has placed before him a deck of specially designed cards. Instead of being like the usual bridge deck, this one consists of 25 cards with only five different designs. The designs used are a circle, a square, a plus sign, a star, and wavy lines.

The "transmitter," or subject with the cards, turns the cards over one by one, concentrating on each for a moment. The other subject, who is the "receiver," tries to tell which design is being contemplated by his colleague.

Each symbol appears five times in random order. By chance alone, a subject might make five correct guesses in 25 attempts. If he were to achieve a higher average consistently, some other factor than chance must be involved in the process. If a subject averages naming seven cards correctly out of 25, for example, this would be highly significant. According to the theory of probability, the odds are at least 500,000 to one against such a high average for a large number of trials.

A number of Duke University students consistently score as high as or higher than this. Dr. Rhine states that on at least one occasion a subject achieved a perfect score, naming all 25 cards correctly.

Dr. Rhine and his associates are also experimenting

80

with *psychokinesis,* which is a scientist's way of saying "mind-over-matter." In order to perform mind-over-matter experiments, Dr. Rhine's group tries to influence the roll of dice. After many hours spent in a moneyless crap game, Dr. Rhine believes that human thoughts can influence events. No one, however, has successfully tested this theory at Las Vegas, although a number of scientists and engineers have tried on occasion.

During the past two years there has been considerable interest in a new and startling phenomenon called "dermo-optical perception," or DOP. As its name suggests, DOP is concerned with the ability to read or at least perceive objects with body parts other than the eyes.

The first concern with DOP in the United States came as a result of the work of Dr. Richard P. Youtz, professor of psychology at Barnard College in New York City. Dr. Youtz had been interested in extrasensory perception phenomena for some time, and in 1963 he happened to hear of the extraordinary powers of Mrs. Patricia Stanley, a housewife from Flint, Michigan.

Mrs. Stanley went to high school in a small town in Kentucky, and one day her teacher asked the students to try to identify objects by touch while blindfolded. Mrs. Stanley was a veritable whiz at this. Not only could she tell what the objects looked like, she could also determine their color. At first the teacher and the other pupils thought she was not blindfolded as well as the others, but she soon demonstrated that she could perform just as well with a brown paper bag tied over her head. Clearly she possessed a power which was not given to everyone.

Her unusual talent went untested, however, until Dr. Youtz heard about her quite by chance. He tested Mrs. Stanley for 60 hours under conditions which ruled out the slightest possibility of fraud.

Her powers were truly amazing. By merely brushing her hands lightly over the surface of objects she could tell their color, and she could even define the shape of designs printed on paper. When asked how she could "see" color with her fingertips, she replied that different colors felt different. Black, for example, was described as being very rough and heavy. Red was sticky, and yellow was slippery, soft, and very light. In general, the lighter colors felt smooth and thin, while the darker ones were rough and heavy.

The Russians have recently published scientific papers about the even more remarkable powers of a young woman named Rosa Kulshova, from the Ural Mountains. Not only can Rosa determine colors while she is blindfolded, but with her fingers she can also read books with large print just about as fast as when her eyes are open. She can read ordinary newspapers through her elbows as well as her fingers, although somewhat more slowly than with her eyes.

One of the most remarkable experiments conducted with Rosa consisted of giving her a green book which was placed under a bright red light. Rosa said the book was blue, which it appeared to be under red lighting. As she rested her hands on the book, the light was suddenly switched off. Rosa was amazed. "The book has changed color," she said. "It has suddenly become green!"

Rosa has even taught her toes to read. She has appeared on Russian TV, and as a result she has attracted several talented rivals to the parlor game of DOP. One of these, perhaps the most talented DOP performer of all, is a 9-year-old girl, Lena Bliznova.

After seeing Rosa's TV broadcast, Lena's mother tested her daughter just for fun. She blindfolded the little girl and placed her before a box of chessmen whose black and white pieces were all jumbled together. The mother was amazed to see her daughter begin separating the black pieces from the white without a moment's hesitation.

Since then Lena has been tested many times and always confounds scientists and doctors by her dazzling and almost supernatural performance. She has been able to see and describe a picture concealed under several books. She can read large letters through her fingertips without touching them at all. At one point she was given a high stack of different-colored papers. By placing her fingers on top of the pile, she called off the order of the colors in the stack without hesitation and without a single mistake.

Lena can see not only with her fingers. From the very start she could read with her shoulders, elbows, the tips of her toes, and even the soles of her feet. She has been able to do everything but duplicate the feat described by O. Henry in one of his stories. He said that the hero had shoes so thin that he could tell the flavor of a piece of chewing gum merely by stepping on it.

Although nobody has been able to taste or smell with their fingers, scientists have long been aware that total human experience was not limited to the individual five senses. As a matter of fact, each sense is made up of a complex grouping of skills and abilities.

In the case of sight, for example, we not only can recognize objects which we have seen before, but we can also distinguish color and estimate distance. We can see in the brightest sunlight and in almost total darkness. Touch also consists of a number of different skills. The ability to distinguish size calls for an altogether different set of sensors from those required to tell if a thing is hot or cold, hard or soft.

Needless to say, the ability to see without eyes did not develop suddenly in the twentieth century. There are many reports of such phenomena which have come down to us from the past. One nineteenth-century character was reportedly able to identify ordinary playing cards when they were placed on his stomach.

Dr. Gregory Razran, head of the psychology department at Queens College in New York City has estimated that better than one in ten persons can be taught to demonstrate some capability with DOP. For those with talent, a number of practice sessions are usually necessary before they can tell colors or describe objects while blindfolded.

How does DOP work?

Scientists have not been able to provide anything other than tentative answers to this question. They know that many of the lower animals have the ability to sense light and darkness through their skins. At least two families of tropical fish are able to generate electrical fields around their bodies. They use the charges generated in these fields to sense the presence of nearby objects.

If DOP is an electrical phenomenon, however, it must depend on types of electrical fields which we are not familiar with at the present time. Charged metal plates

83

have been used in some of the experiments, and while these have affected the performance of the subjects, the results have not been predictable or consistent with any known electrical field theory.

Attempts have been made to explain DOP on the basis of the radiation of light and heat. Indeed, a number of the most talented DOP subjects have been able to perform better in lighted rooms than in darkness. They have described the sensations which have enabled them to distinguish colors in terms of the warmth of the object. However, these theories also have not been entirely satisfactory. For example, they do not explain how the little Russian girl, Lena, was able to describe a picture buried under a number of books or read off the colors of sheets of paper in a stack.

Another area of research was described very briefly at the Fourteenth International Astronautics Federation meeting in Paris recently by Dr. Eugene B. Konecci of the National Aeronautics and Space Administration. Dr. Konecci stated that Russian scientists have established at least eight research centers specializing in what he called "thought transference over distance" and "electronic hypnotizers."

He then went on to say that studies of the possibilities inherent in such phenomena are being carried out in both the United States and Russia. NASA is interested because they might prove to be useful in our space exploration programs.

A well-known U.S. physician specializing in the study of nervous systems, Dr. Andrija Puharich, has suggested some ideas for developing the practical usefulness of extrasensory perception. Dr. Puharich feels that the thought-transference phenomenon is affected by gravity, and would like to try some experiments with a man in space where a gravity-free condition could be maintained for a long period.

Dr. Puharich points out that in the region between the earth and the moon there is an area where the gravitational attraction of each body is equal. He theorizes that this would be an ideal place to orbit a space laboratory from which to conduct energy-transfer experiments toward the earth.

In his experiments, Dr. Puharich would place the human receiver in the space laboratory. The sender would remain on earth and would be subjected to the high gravitational forces of the surface. If Dr. Puharich's theory is correct we should find a most remarkable increase in "mind reading" or thought transference under such conditions.

Like DOP, the phenomenon of thought transference has been known to exist for many generations. In spite of the vast number of experiments which have been conducted and the large number of persons who have evidenced some capability to read minds, it has not been possible to control the process well enough to allow the development of practical applications, nor can we explain how it works.

Perhaps we are in the same position in relation to extrasensory perception today as we were to radio only a few years ago. At least there are no current theories which adequately explain all the extrasensory experiments in terms of known physical laws. One can speculate that perhaps we are just on the edge of sensory capabilities which depend upon natural principles that we do not understand yet.

Somewhere in the universe there may be higher forms of life than ourselves who can make daily use of such phenomena—life which is not bounded and limited as we are. As we slowly climb the evolutionary ladder, perhaps we also may learn to reach further into this mysterious world beyond our senses.

10 | ON THE THRESHOLD OF SPACE

We alone of all earthly creatures are aware of the movements of the planets and the vast order of the natural world. We have little kinship with the other life forms around us, having left them far behind. We are lonely in the realization that we are isolated on our small world, marooned on an island in the endless void of space.

We have gone far enough to know that beneath the solid world of our senses lie strange forces which none of us understand, operating over distances we do not comprehend. The earth is a small planet, and the universe is incredibly vast. Our spirits and our imagination already soar far beyond the confines of this humble globe.

The chemical and biological changes which have formed a part of our fantastically lucky heritage would not of themselves have carried us to our present high pinnacle. True, they have provided us with a most marvelous construction, so that we are both curious and intelligent, as well as ambitious and retentive.

Not only are we capable, we are also technical. It is this ability to progress along technological lines that has brought us the ultimate victory over environment.

Galileo dropped two stones from a tower and needed to do no more, but a manned flight to Mars can be achieved only after many expensive preliminary launches. Low cost and high reliability have not proved to be compatible characteristics in today's scientific environment.

The two factors of cost and reliability are the most important considerations that will continue to trouble us as we seek to explore space. And the one is closely related to the other. Cost is high because a space ship must be made thoroughly reliable to avoid failures which would lead to even greater cost.

Fortune magazine has estimated that our national space budget will be no less than $20 billion by 1970. It has now become obvious that any worthwhile exploration of space is far beyond the capabilities of all but the larger nations. In many ways this is an unfortunate situation, because the conquest of space is a human endeavor and not a national one.

A pamphlet called "Space—The New Frontier," published recently by the National Aeronautics and Space Administration, contains the following paragraph: "Man will establish permanent stations in space—laboratories, observatories, experimental testing platforms and way stations. He will visit the Moon, Venus and Mars. He will

86

send probes to more distant planets and even the far distant stars. He will probably discover that life exists in space. He may communicate with other beings in space. Regardless of what form his exploration takes or what other results he may achieve, man's greatest benefits will still be the knowledge he brings back for the benefit of mankind."

Five years earlier such words would have branded their author as a visionary quite removed from the practical world. But the pace of scientific achievement has become so swift that the visions of the morning have become the reality of the afternoon.

From time immemorial, man has gazed at the heavens, worshipfully at first, and then with wonder and curiosity. As long as the earth itself lay unconquered, the conquest of the heavens was but the most inaccessible of many frontiers which challenged his spirit. Each step toward the conquest of this planet still left intact the mysteries of the sky. But as the frontiers of the earth faded away, those of space grew more tantalizing until, in our century, man has become obsessed with the challenge. Once the age of flight was under way, man immediately began to dream of ways to attack the blue-vaulted prison above him.

One such dream was that of a young man named David Lasser, who in 1930 joined with 11 other young men to form a group with an ambitious title: The American Interplanetary Society. During the summer of 1931, David Lasser gathered with his friends to blast off home-made rockets on the sands of Staten Island. They were temperamental and unpredictable gadgets, powered by liquid oxygen and gasoline. Sometimes they rose to altitudes of 50 feet; sometimes they did not rise at all, but died in their own smoke, smoldering on the hot sand.

Compared to the dream, these missiles were sorry experimental fact. They had no guidance, and one of the thrills of the day involved escaping the launched rockets once they did leave the ground.

The reality was weak, but the dream persisted. In 1931, in a book called *The Conquest of Space*, David Lasser wrote: "Perhaps by 1950 the brilliant project of Hermann Oberth (an Austrian scientist) for a station

87

in space may be interesting the world-wide attention of engineers. The proposal of Oberth to build an artificial satellite of the earth, if found feasible, may provide the mental and physical stepping stone from our conquest of the earth to that of the solar system."

Not long ago, David Lasser said: "It was all kind of a dream at that time. I'm astounded that we have progressed so fast."

There were other dreamers. One was laughingly called the "moon-rocket man" by the press of his day. This was Dr. Robert H. Goddard, who is known in these somewhat more enlightened times as the father of modern rocketry. Dr. Goddard began his experiments before World War I with very little money and practically no encouragement. His wife helped with his experiments by sewing the special parachutes needed to slow the descent of the scientific instruments he sent aloft with his rockets.

March 16, 1926, was a milestone for Goddard. He launched the first liquid-fueled rocket. The reaction of observers who witnessed this epoch-making flight is not recorded, but there was probably no wild enthusiasm, since the rocket flew for only 2½ seconds. It staggered upward no higher than a four-story building, and traveled a distance of only 200 feet at a speed of 60 miles per hour. A rather feeble demonstration for a man who was said to be bent on flying to the moon!

Because of the unfavorable publicity given to crackpot schemes such as space flight, Dr. Goddard was reluctant to have the results of his experiments published. Consequently, this first liquid-fueled rocket escaped the notice of all but a few scientists. It must be recorded, however, that Goddard's trail-blazing efforts did not come to naught. During the past few years, many thousands of liquid-fueled rockets have been flown to extreme altitudes and into orbits around the moon and the planets—performances which were only dreamed of by the professor.

Dr. Goddard did not live to receive the recognition which should have been accorded his achievements. His later work, however, resulted in the famed bazooka used against tanks in World War II.

At the same time, experiments with rockets were going on in other countries. Among the experimenters was an unknown Russian schoolteacher, Konstantin Eduardovich Tsiolkovsky. History does not tell us whether his complete obscurity outside Russia exists because of the difficulty of his name or because of the general lack of interest concerning the exploration of space which lasted throughout most of his lifetime. But, as future events were to demonstrate conclusively, Mr. Tsiolkovsky was a pathfinder in the field of space travel.

He taught high school mathematics for most of his life in the provincial Russian town of Kaluga, and worked in utter loneliness. Tsiolkovsky had no contact with scientists, and most of his early research years were spent in rediscovering advances which had already been made by others. Around the turn of the century, he developed the theory of liquid-fueled rockets and designed several of these systems. By 1929 this self-taught Russian had suggested putting two or three rockets together and in this way achieving results which were impossible with one rocket by itself. Unfortunately, he did not live to see the application of his theories in such programs as Mercury, Gemini, and Apollo.

Soviet scientists have also credited Mr. Tsiolkovsky with being the first to recommend the satellite and to suggest that it might become a way station in space. He had received little recognition from the Czarist regime, but was honored greatly by the Soviets before his death in 1935, and the centenary of his birth was celebrated with considerable fanfare on September 17, 1957.

During the Twenties and Thirties, interest began to develop in Russia concerning rockets and the possibilities of space flight. Professor Nikolai Rynin of the University of Leningrad wrote nine books which summed up all the knowledge existing at that time, and these were published in the early Thirties.

The first Russian rocket society, The Group for Investigation of Reaction Motion, was organized in November, 1929. During World War II, the Russians developed the multibarreled Katyusha rockets and used them with good effect against the Germans.

In 1927, in the town of Breslau, Germany, a group was formed with the name of *Verein für Raumschiffahrt*— The Society for Space Travel. Dr. Hermann Oberth was an early member of this society. Already Oberth had written a book that had achieved a certain commercial if not critical success. Its title was *The Rocket Into Interplanetary Space*. But the time was not ripe for full scientific acceptance of Oberth's theories, and there is a faint suspicion that his book sold for somewhat the same reasons that science fiction is popular today. It was from this book that David Lasser was to draw his prophetic conclusions in 1931.

During these pioneer days, the early rocket experimenters found themselves involved in all sorts of foolish and time-consuming controversies. Many fell into the same category as the famous argument of the Middle Ages concerning how many angels could sit on the head of a pin. Others were based on ludicrous and absurd misconceptions about natural law.

Several prominent physicists have totally demolished Oberth's theories, they felt, by stating that "everyone knows space flight is impossible because there is nothing for the exhaust gases to push against in airless space."

The idea was that a space ship, once it traveled beyond the atmosphere, would skid to a stop, like a car which has lost traction on an icy road. Just how "everyone" could "know" this fallacy was never brought out. In any case, a simple experiment based on Newton's law of motion is sufficient to demonstrate the error of this argument.

One of these distinguished gentlemen had a reputation as a hunter. He was asked if he thought his shotgun would still recoil against his shoulder in outer space. After some thought, he conceded that it would, because the acceleration of the shot must exert an equal and opposite reaction on the gun.

A whole series of arguments revolved around Oberth's statement that it was possible for a rocket to exceed the velocity of its own exhaust gases. A number of scientists of considerable standing felt that this would require a motor capable of attaining an efficiency of more than 100 per cent. They classified any such idea in the same category as palm reading or schemes for achieving perpetual motion. In truth, no rocket motor ever attains an efficiency even approaching 100 per cent, whether it exceeds its exhaust gas velocity or not—and many do.

As a result of such buffoonery and, it must also be admitted, because of many unsolved technical difficulties, it was not considered scientific in those days to talk seriously of the exploration of space, either by radio or by space ships. All things must wait their time.

Dr. Goddard and some of the other rocket men preferred anonymity to charges of quackery, and therefore made themselves unavailable to newspaper reporters—not the first time that scientists have found themselves at odds with the press. In 1934, the American Interplanetary Society, its members weary of being laughed at, changed its name to the American Rocket Society to gain a small measure of scientific respectability. It has since joined forces with an organization devoted to aircraft engineering, and now enjoys the imposing title of The American Institute of Aeronautics and Astronautics.

The old American Interplanetary Society had been a sickly organization with limited membership, few friends, and no money. There was no central office, and no national organization. Its members—students, hobbyists, and a few college professors—met in their own homes. They may have regarded themselves as practical visionaries, but they were looked upon by their contemporaries as mad dreamers. Things change.

Before it recently joined with the Institute for Aeronautics, the American Rocket Society's home offices took up a good share of one floor at 500 Fifth Avenue in New York City, in the heart of Manhattan's highly regarded business section, employed enough full-time people to administer a medium-size manufacturing concern, and on its membership rolls were some of the most respected names of science and the aviation industry. American businessmen, always quick to sense future trends, sponsored memberships for their engineers at company cost.

This is a far cry indeed from the early, lonely days of Goddard and Oberth, whose work continued without spectacular result until the beginning of World War II. Oberth's calculations made him aware of a few hard realities, which have been both the plague and the dream of rocket scientists ever since. In order for a rocket to leave the earth's magnetic grasp, according to Oberth, it must achieve a certain "escape velocity."

Once this escape velocity is attained, no more propellant is needed. The rocket will coast indefinitely, without power into the soundless reaches of outer space, borne outward by its own inertia. It will remain in straight-line motion forever unless it is trapped by the gravitational field of some other body, such as the sun.

The search for better rocket fuels has resulted in some of the most intensive research of our time. Thousands of chemists and propulsion engineers spend millions of hours each year searching through all the minerals in the earth's crust for better, more powerful fuels.

The progress made in recent years toward solving this difficult problem of finding better fuels can best be illustrated by the following comparison. Dr. Goddard once calculated the fuel and motor weights required to lift one pound of payload 230 miles off the surface of the earth. This calculation used fuels available in 1920, and it turned out that a fuel and motor weight about 6 times the total mass of the earth would be required to do the job! No wonder the early rocketeers worked in an atmosphere of derision and discouragement.

Only 29 years later, in February 1949, a Bumper-Wac missile rose to a height of 250 miles, carrying a payload of nearly 15 tons—considerably more than the one pound payload which according to Goddard's calculations was impossible.

The propellant problem has given rise to the term "mass ratio," which means the ratio of the weight of a rocket when empty to its weight when fully fueled. The problem of fitting a container around a rocket which is light enough to give an acceptable mass ratio, and at the same time can contain beings of some intelligence and sufficient strength to withstand the rigors of acceleration and the unknown environment outside the earth's atmosphere, has kept most of the available rocket talent busy during this century. The history of rocket flight has been, among other things, a slow and painstaking history of achieving better mass ratios. Fortunately, it has been possible to reach mass ratios which are capable of carrying men and instruments to the moon and nearby planets. But the possibilities for journeying outside our solar system are still quite remote. The distances are too great, and man's span of life is too brief.

The first real hint, outside the research laboratories of Peenemünde, Germany, that man's ancient dream of space flight might develop into reality, came during the turbulent, rumor-filled war year of 1944. The German propaganda machine of Dr. Josef Goebbels commenced a great campaign about "secret weapons" which would soon accomplish what the Luftwaffe had failed to do, namely, bring England to her knees by virtue of their terrible destructive power.

In June of that year, there occurred a mysterious air burst near the town of Kalmar in Sweden. Because of the tremendous altitude and the ballistic trajectory of the object, it was at first assumed by the local people that the explosion had been caused by some sort of meteor. However, strange reports soon began to arrive from the farmers in the area. Part of a rocket fin was brought to the authorities, then a piece of the motor and the rocket shell. All the pieces were gathered together, flown to England, and analyzed by Allied scientists. The evidence was inescapable. The Germans had invented some sort of long-range rocket.

The first V-2 fell on England during the evening of September 8, 1944, and Winston Churchill disclosed its existence in the House of Commons in November. By this time, London and the surrounding English country-side were already painfully aware that all was not propaganda about the "Vengeance Weapons," as Goebbels called them.

In this unhappy fashion, news of the first man-conceived flight outside the earth's heavier atmosphere reverberated through the capitals of the world. We can perhaps forgive the statesmen of the time if they did not immediately realize that the Vengeance Weapon was the harbinger of a great new age of exploration into the fathomless void beyond the earth.

Although it did not win the war, as forecast by the voluble Dr. Goebbels, the V-2 was something new in warfare, as the crossbow had been 15 centuries before, and as the atomic bomb was to become only a few months later. While its devastation was not equal to that of the heaviest bombs, the V-2 was a psychological weapon of terrible proportions. It struck entirely without warning. It had no capability to discriminate between hospitals, schools, churches, or bomber airfields; it was as likely to hit one as the other.

In substance, the launching of the first V-2 added up to one of those moments when the human world achieves a perceptible movement from the place where it has been. A movement, small but distinct, which can never be retraced. For better or for worse, things were changed, and they could never be quite the same for any of us again.

After the war, a great deal was learned about the V-2 rockets. They had the appearance of true space ships, being 46 feet long, shaped like a cigar, and pointing directly upward during launch. At take-off the V-2 grossed over 14 tons, while the empty rocket plus warhead weighed about 4 tons as it came hurtling down on London; thus it had a mass ratio of better than 3 to 1. Unlike the V-1 pulse-jet flying bomb, the V-2 was unstoppable, once it was launched. It reached an altitude of over 50 miles and had a maximum range of about 200 miles.

To the people of Britain, the factor of most significance about the Vengeance Weapons was their speed. At impact, the missile traveled at the rate of a mile per second. During the London blitz a reporter calculated that an observer, if he started running at the very instant the missile became visible to the naked eye, could take exactly 7 steps before the 2,000-pound warhead would destroy him.

Because of their terrible speed—far beyond anything man had been able to create before—neither guns nor fighter aircraft were effective against them. Nor was any other protective device that the Allies were able to devise capable of diverting any one of the hundreds of V-2 missiles that were fired against the British homeland.

But the V-2 would have no place in a chronicle about the search for extraterrestrial life if it had been merely a new weapon. It was an achievement not only for warfare, but also in a far more significant direction. For the first time, man had put together in one package the elements necessary for flight beyond his atmospheric prison. The V-2 demonstrated the practicality of this greatest of all adventures.

When Hermann Oberth was told in 1955 that we would soon be able to launch space satellites, basing them on the V-2, he replied: "There must not only be one but many of these, each a little larger and more revealing than its predecessor. Small animals will go up in them first, then large animals, and finally a man—the pioneer in space. How I wish I could be that man! Columbus, Magellan, Balboa, all the great adventurers of the past will be only shadows behind him in the history books of tomorrow."

Today we can say almost with certainty that our first contact with living things born elsewhere than on this earth will come as a result of these first rocket programs. Although the life we find may not be anything like ours, surely not as complicated or as well developed, it will demonstrate two fundamental qualities: growth and reproduction.

We will discover this life in our solar system with robots landed on other planets, using rockets which are now being constructed.

The satellites and space probes which we have launched are new beacons, competing with the antique light of the distant stars. Their faint returning voices are a thrilling achievement and symbolize a great victory for man. But these voices also carry a warning which none of us can afford to ignore.

Man possesses a fierce, questing, competitive spirit which is his heritage from the long dark past. This spirit built the ancient fires, placed television sets in our homes, and has led to mastery of the world. It has also brought us to the position where we can no longer squabble over the real estate of the earth.

The restless spirit within us has generated perhaps the greatest paradox of all time. On the one hand we must continue to move forward and outward, for biologically the static forms have always been at a disadvantage and few have survived. At the same time we must restrain our hereditary instinct to prevail. Can we do it?

Like the blind, deep-sea shellfish at the bottom of the ocean, man crawls about crab-like on the surface of his earth. Only lately and with great difficulty has he learned to swim in the lower layers of his atmosphere, and his humble attempts to break the shackles of gravity are only now beginning to bear fruit. During all the long past, the best he could do was to peer upward at the eternal sky with its great rivers of stars, blink his inadequate eyes, and perhaps speculate a little.

Among scientists, the astronomer has had the most opportunity for experiencing humility. Each clear night the universe preaches a sermon on human inadequacy, and no one is in a better position to understand it than the professional stargazer.

There have been three great milestones in the history of astronomy, and two of them have occurred in this century. The initial giant step forward was taken by Galileo in 1609 when he trained the first crude telescope on the stars and detected the moons of Jupiter and the phases of Venus. The second was in 1932 when Jansky invented, or perhaps we should say discovered, radio astronomy with his antenna mounted on the axle of a Model-T Ford.

Galileo demonstrated that we could collect the rays of light and magnify the images of the stars optically so that we could see them in more detail. Jansky discovered that by listening carefully we could hear "star talk"—the noise which the stars generate on the radio frequencies. This gave astronomy a new dimension which opened many unexplored avenues of investigation. The introduction of the radio telescope was most timely, because it was rapidly becoming apparent that conventional visual astronomy had just about reached the end of its potential. Astronomers were still, however, building larger and

96

larger telescopes; even now the Russians are said to be putting the finishing touches on a 236-inch mirror. But in recent years the results have not been very encouraging. Astronomers realize that a large percentage of the starlight is blocked off from their view by the atmosphere, and that this deep sea of air blurs and distorts the images in their best instruments so that they shimmer and shake like the headlights of a car moving over a rough road. This is particularly true in the larger telescopes at high magnification.

In addition, much light is scattered by the atmosphere, and this diffused starlight ultimately fogs the astronomer's photographic plates even on the darkest nights, thus limiting the length of his exposures. For this reason it is impossible to photograph the extremely faint stars and the galaxies which lie far out at the edge of space.

The force of gravity bends and distorts the carefully curved optical surfaces and destroys the precise alignment of the largest instruments. This has limited the practical upper limit of their size just at the point where things were really beginning to get interesting.

The electromagnetic spectrum, which is the broad highway down which all our knowledge of the radio universe must flow, is a wide band of frequencies with the extremely short gamma rays on one end and the long waves of radio on the other. About a million times a million gamma rays would be required to reach one inch, while the longest radio frequencies have waves 500 miles long.

Visible light occupies a thin band of frequency spectrum that is about one-third of the way from the gamma ray end. It is only slightly more than one per cent of the length of the electronic spectrum. Until the discovery of Jansky, however, astronomers were limited to this narrow strip of frequency pavement. Radio astronomy added another 5.5 per cent of the spectrum at the short end of the radio frequencies, so that we were now able to make use of three quarters of one per cent of the total. Even if we had the instruments to exploit fully the gamma rays, X-rays, ultraviolet light, and longer radio waves, we could not do so because the atmosphere blocks these frequencies as effectively as would a stone wall.

Except for a narrow band of about one per cent in the near infrared, we can never hope to use any more of the spectrum, as long as our instruments must peer upward from the surface of the earth. This infrared window, however, has one extremely important attribute. It allows us to obtain an indication of the temperature of other bodies, since temperature is more easily related to the infrared radiation.

Having come this far, the world of astronomy was now ready for the third major milestone, which became an accomplished fact in 1946.

In this year Dr. Richard Tousey of the Naval Research Laboratory mounted a small spectrograph in the nose of one of the captured V-2 German missiles. The rocket reached an altitude high above the stratosphere over White Sands Proving Ground in New Mexico and brought back the spectral record of the sun's ultraviolet radiation. For the first time, man was able to move his instruments outside the blurring cloak of atmosphere.

This new victory was made even more complete during the summer of 1957, when Dr. Martin Schwartzschild of Princeton University launched his Stratoscope I balloon and obtained the best pictures ever made of the sun. Stratoscope I snapped its pictures from an altitude of about 15 miles.

Balloons can achieve altitudes of about 100,000 feet, which is above more than 95 per cent of the atmosphere. This allows them to open up the entire electromagnetic spectrum from wave lengths just above those of visible light and the middle frequency radio waves, about 35 per cent of the total. The shorter wave lengths are absorbed by the free oxygen even at these high altitudes, while the longer waves are reflected by the ionosphere's electrons.

But balloons are not enough, nor are instruments placed in the noses of rockets that rise briefly into space and then fall back again. What we really need are steady platforms in space, far above the atmosphere and free of the effects of gravity.

The National Aeronautics and Space Administration recognized this requirement early in its short history. As a result of the NASA interest, the first true space-observing platform was launched on March 7, 1962. It was called the Orbital Solar Observatory, or OSO, and was designed to radio back to earth its view of the sun from outer space. John C. Lindsey of the Goddard Space Flight Center has obtained many valuable hours of data from this first space observatory, far more than the few brief moments that were available from the V-2 probes. A second platform, the Orbital Geophysical Observatory or OGO, was launched in the summer of 1964, and has told us even more about the vast store of radiation which can be sensed by instruments located outside the atmospheric wall.

These satellites are only the first of many to come. Neither of them contain telescopes or the large sophisticated instruments which have become the backbone of modern astronomy.

Astronomers all over the world are extremely excited over these first experiments and have become ardent space cadets. Until recently, theirs has been a cold and lonely science with much time spent on isolated mountain tops. A good deal of their lives has passed in frustrated waiting—for the clouds to disappear, for night to come, for the moon to fall below the horizon, and for the stars to swing into a favorable position.

With the advent of the space observatory, they can now foresee the end of this sort of existence. Instruments in space controlled by earth-bound astronomers will allow the astronomer to combine his labors with those of other scientists, since such devices will require the united efforts of skilled technologists in a variety of different fields.

Instead of making his observations from a mountain-top observatory whose temperature must be the same as that of the surrounding atmosphere in order to preserve the optical alignment, he can do his work in the comfort of an air-conditioned control station. He need no longer worry about the weather; even night and day will appear the same to a telescope located in the eternal darkness of space beyond the atmospheric glow. Perhaps best of all, the view will always be superb, unhampered by the cluttered disorder of the sea of air.

But how much better is a space observatory than an earth-bound one? Will it really be able to help us solve the riddle of life on other worlds?

Anyone who has had the opportunity to view one of the planets through a large telescope has probably come away with at least a mild feeling of frustration. The direct images are generally not at all like the relatively sharp retouched photos we find in the modern science magazines. The bright disk shimmers and shakes like the image of the lights around a pool mirrored in the water after the swimmers have passed. A peculiar tracery weaves and bends somewhere between eye and object as though a thin film of oil covered the objective lens.

If one is lucky, there will be a magic, breathless moment when the image clears and for a brief instant the disk will look as it should look, distinct, sharp, well-defined. It was no doubt during just such a moment that Schiaparelli caught the first tantalizing glimpse of his famous and controversial canals on Mars.

This shimmering effect of the atmosphere is explained by the astronomer in terms of what he calls "angular resolution." Angular resolution can be thought of as the angle which must exist between two stars before they will be seen as two distant and separate objects. About the best such resolution which can be obtained by an earth-bound photographic telescope is about one-third of a second of arc. This value is obtained only during rare intervals. For this reason most clear pictures of the planets have been made by taking a large number of exposures with a form of movie camera and then picking out the best of them. Very few of the total are actually of any value.

Even this best of all seeing is no better than the theoretical capability of a perfect 12-inch telescope. This explains why the construction of huge modern telescopes has not produced corresponding spectacular discoveries in visual astronomy.

Just as it limited the capability and life span of the ancient dinosaurs, gravity has placed a restriction on the useful size of modern telescopes. In order to be most effective, an optical surface must have no imperfections greater than one-tenth of the wave length of light, a matter of some two-millionths of an inch. The larger the mirror, the more it is warped and bent by the strong pull of gravity as it follows the cosmic pathways of the stars. A 200-inch telescope is considered by most designers to be very nearly the ultimate in size, because of present-day limitations in materials and engineering.

No other science is so much in need of new instruments and techniques as astronomy. We have already reached the limits of visual earth-bound astronomy, and are rapidly approaching them in radio astronomy. Astronomers have reached these stops because of two major factors, atmosphere and gravity.

Both obstacles will be removed by establishing observatories in space. For all practical purposes, the atmospheric blight will disappear at an altitude of 300 miles, and the gravitational problem will be surmounted merely by placing an Orbiting Astronomical Observatory in the weightless environment of orbit. In the tradition of the early grade-B movies, technology has overtaken the astronomer's greatest problems just as they were about to stifle him.

The first large telescope to be placed in orbit will be a 36-inch mirror, which should be launched in 1967. In order to make maximum use of its opportunities, this instrument must be very carefully designed and constructed. Its primary mirror must present the most perfect surface that modern telescope makers can produce. A similar instrument has been sent aloft in Stratoscope II, the high-altitude balloon project succeeding Stratoscope I.

To be most effective, these instruments should be capable of an angular resolution of about one-tenth of a second of arc. This will require that the guidance system be capable of maintaining a track with an accuracy within this limit. While such precision is a formidable design task when it must be attained in a satellite traveling at 5 miles per second at an altitude of 500 miles, it is not impossible. The design specifications have already been met for Stratoscope II.

The orbit of the OAO must be known within precise limits if it is to track the stars with the required accuracy. Its orbital altitude of 500 miles has been selected very carefully, with many factors in mind. It is high enough to be above almost all the atmospheric drag, and yet is below the region of the Van Allen belt which would bombard the observatory with distracting radiation.

No doubt some future astronomer will want to place his telescopes in an observatory that will remain directly over his head instead of revolving around the earth like a moon. This will be made possible by merely installing a satellite in an orbit whose period is the same as the rotational period of the earth—about 24 hours. The altitude for such an OAO is approximately 22,500 miles. From the astronomer's point of view this will be like having an observatory on a mountain top over 22,500 miles high, without the discomforts of living at such an altitude.

What sort of results can be expected from this 36-inch instrument orbiting in space, and how will they compare with those of the best earth-bound telescopes?

The area of the 36-inch telescope will be about one-thirtieth as large as that of the Mount Palomar 200-inch one. Therefore, one would expect that exposures 30 times as long would be required to produce images of stars as faint as those which are at the edge of 200-inch visibility, where the great telescope becomes limited by the sky background.

However, this is not the case. The photographic plates of the space telescope will not be fogged at all by the air glow which affects the larger earth-bound instruments. Nor will they be subjected to the shimmer which reduces the angular resolution. Because of these factors the pictures from the OAO 36-inch telescope are expected to compare favorably with those available from the 200-inch which are taken with the same exposure. Since much longer exposure times can be obtained with the 36-inch, the ultimate capability of this instrument should be considerably greater.

No doubt whole galaxies will be discovered by the OAO, glittering like diamonds beyond the limits of our present vision. Much detail within the star structures which we already know is sure to be seen for the first time. The limits of the known universe are certain to be pushed outward by many light years.

The greatest gain from the OAO will come from the additional wave lengths which can be recorded through its clear eye. Ultraviolet pictures of nebulae and star clusters have almost invariably shown a great deal more detailed structure than those in the region of visible light. Once the optical window is widened by flight above the atmospheric filter, even more wonders will doubtless become visible. Most of the energy radiated in the frequency band near that of light is at ultraviolet wave lengths.

A more interesting wave length to view stars by is the very short one of X-rays. Perhaps sometime in the future this may lead to an Orbital X-ray Observatory, or OXO. Because X-rays are extremely short, they produce very sharp images. In theory, X-rays would be a thousand times more efficient than visible light for telescopic observations. In effect, this means that a telescope with a diameter of only one-fifth of an inch could resolve to the theoretical limits of the 200-inch telescope if it could operate at X-ray frequencies.

Unfortunately, X-rays are extremely difficult to work with. They can be photographed only with difficulty, and are not subject to the same bending which allows conventional optical systems to focus ordinary light. Indeed, a focal length of more than 50 feet would be required to focus the moderately short X-rays collected by an objective lens of one-inch aperture. This problem is being studied by a number of different scientists, and already designs have been proposed for an X-ray microscope.

It is one thing to take pictures of the stars through a telescope launched into a deep space orbit, but quite another to deliver such pictures to the eager astronomers who are confined to the earth. How do the stargazers propose to collect their negatives?

There are a number of different techniques for doing this, some of which have already been proven by such experiments as the Russian Lunik, or Cosmic Rocket III, launched on October 4, 1959. This missile took the first photos ever made of the back side of the moon.

According to the Russian scientists who conducted the

103

experiment, these pictures were first photographed through an ordinary camera. Then they were developed and scanned by a conventional TV transmitter, and the results of this scan were placed on magnetic tape and stored within the satellite. As Lunik III swung back in her orbit toward earth, the taped pictures were transmitted back to Russia via radio. Although much better pictures could be transmitted back to earth now, it is not absolutely necessary to transmit pictures at all. The information can be returned to earth in the form of numbers representing different intensities across the scan pattern. These numbers can be interpreted by the scientists just as easily as pictures can, and the numbers will actually provide more data. Unfortunately for those of us who feel that there should be a connection between science and art, astronomy is progressing away from the situation where the subject under study is examined in all its breath-taking beauty through an eyepiece or by means of a color photographic plate.

Many mysteries of the cosmos will be solved by the OAO's, and they will doubtless generate new puzzles which will take the place of the old ones. Among the questions which we can have reason to hope will be answered are a great many which have a bearing on the search for life on other planets.

For example, as we have discussed in earlier chapters, it is quite impossible to see the planets of other stars. Indeed, we are unable to resolve the disks of the stars themselves because of their vast distance from us. In every case they appear as brief points of light, even though William Herschel said when he first saw Sirius through his largest telescope: "The glare of this object reflected from the speculum was like the magnificent light of the rising sun."

During the early days of the telescope it was not uncommon for astronomers to report that they had observed the planets of other stars. About 1780, Christian Mayer, a celebrated German astronomer, made the claim that he had seen clusters of planets surrounding a number of distant stars. Most other scientists felt that Mayer was wrong, and the issue was hotly debated. Since Mayer's alleged discovery occurred long before the invention of photography, really conclusive proof was very difficult.

Today we can prove quite easily that the planets of other stars cannot be seen from the earth. Jupiter, for example, is the largest of our sun's planets. Its orbit lies more than 450 million miles from the sun, and Jupiter's diameter is almost one-tenth that of the sun. Perhaps it might seem that the nearby astronomers of other solar systems might be able to identify Jupiter through their telescopes, but such is probably not the case.

Jupiter does not shine with a light of its own but merely by the reflected light from the sun. It is therefore a much fainter object, and the great radiated energy of the sun would blot out the weak reflections of the planet unless there were some way of effectively masking the sun's mighty light.

Even if this could be done, a 200-inch telescope would not be enough. It would require a 300-inch mirror of the best quality in order to see a planet the size of Jupiter revolving around a distant star, although it might be photographed through a smaller instrument.

A telescope for this purpose could not be based on a planet like the earth with an atmosphere. It must be placed in orbit like the OAO, or put on an airless moon.

We shouldn't, however, discount the possibility of being able to perform such a feat in the not too distant future. We are on the threshold of a bright new era of astronomy. Before the end of this century, we will place some truly remarkable scientific instruments in space. Large astronomical telescopes will soon be in orbit and a lunar observatory may be a reality.

In an earlier chapter it was mentioned that there are other things besides telescopes which can be used to find the planets of far-off stars. With a great deal of luck, we might do this by detecting the variation in the radiation of a star as its planets move across its face during a planetary eclipse.

In 1834 a German astronomer named Friedrich Bessel became fascinated by the motion of the brightest star in the sky, Sirius. Bessel had studied the path of this beautiful object through his telescopes and found that Sirius did not travel in a straight line. Like a slightly drunken man on his way home after pay day, the star seemed to weave a little. Not much, but just enough so that Bessel could be sure that he was not "seeing things" —an occupational hazard of astronomers in those days.

Bessel studied and charted the motion of Sirius for ten years. At the end of that time, he was not only certain the star did not travel in a straight line but he was also quite confident that he knew why. Sirius was shadowed by an unseen companion whose attraction pulled it back and forth so that it seemed to stagger a bit in its orbit.

Since his best telescopes failed to reveal this companion of Sirius, Bessel was forced to conclude that it was smaller than the parent star, extremely dense, and did not emit very much light. It appeared to complete an orbit around Sirius every 50 years.

Almost 20 years later, in 1862, the son of Alvan Clark, who was perhaps the best lens-maker of all time, was testing a new 18-inch telescope which had just been completed by his father. By pure chance he happened to direct the instrument toward Sirius. He was the first human being to actually see the faint companion star which had been predicted by Bessel so many years before.

Since the middle of the nineteenth century, a number of companions have been located around stars in our general vicinity. These have not been planets, however, since they generate heat and light and are far too large. The objects which we call planets are much smaller than companion stars. The total mass of all the planets in the solar system is little more than one-thousandth as much as that of the sun itself.

In 1963 Dr. Peter van de Kamp of the Sproul Observatory at Swarthmore College made a most interesting discovery while looking for more companion stars. He noted a faint, almost imperceptible wave in the track of Barnard's star on one of his photographic plates. Using the extreme precision which photography has provided for the astronomer, he was able to calculate the size of this small object.

The dark companion of Barnard's star is most unlikely to be seen by any telescope located on our own planet, because it is only half again as large as Jupiter. Although it is large and rather massive to be the home of life as we know it, this object is, indisputably, a planet; perhaps a potential home for life belonging to a solar system other than our own.

Although we know almost nothing about the planets of other stars, there can be little doubt about their existence. The tools for discovering more about them are rapidly taking shape. Long before the end of this century we will have learned much more. This knowledge will surely herald a quickening interest in the search for intelligent life on other worlds.

Harlow Shapley and others have suggested that life may exist on bodies which, unlike the earth, are not satellites of a sun. True, such planets would not have the life-giving radiation from a mothering sun, but does this rule out all possibility of life? Shapley doesn't think so. The amount of heat which is generated by any celestial body is a function of its size and mass. It is quite logical that many bodies exist in space which are too small to glow like stars —and are thus visually undetectable—but are still large enough to provide the necessary warmth for life. Shapley has calculated that the proper size for such a dark world would be at least 10 times that of Jupiter.

Life on such a lonely, nomadic earth as this would be very different from ours. Eyes which use radiation between the infrared and ultraviolet wave lengths would be quite useless, and the hampering force of gravity would have a much greater effect. As Shapley has said: "The imagination boggles at the possibility of self-warming planets that do not depend, as we do, on the inefficient process of getting warmth through radiation from a sun millions of miles away. What strange creatures might develop on such a world!"

What we know of the great domain beyond the immediate vicinity of our own planet has come to us mainly through the faculty of sight. With the advent of radio astronomy after World War II, we also began to learn about the universe through its sounds.

Both sight and sound, however, are frustrating in their incompleteness. Their products are filtered and warped and changed. The great blanket of atmosphere acts as a board of censorship, rigorous and inflexible. While censors may possibly be desirable in the arts, they are a quite unnecessary vexation in science.

In addition, the stars are remote and our instruments are weak. Our knowledge would be much more complete if we could go and visit them, or better still, if they could come and visit us, considering the rigors of a long space voyage.

Recently, Nobel Prize winner Dr. Harold Urey of the University of California described what he called "potentially the most interesting and indeed astounding fact of all scientific study in recent years." He was not talking of a sweeping new physical theory which would revolutionize the concepts of Einstein, nor was he interested in some discovery of fuels or materials which might lead to very much improved automobiles.

Dr. Urey was commenting about the possible implications of some exciting research which is currently being carried on by a number of scientists on a small pile of rather nondescript rocks. There are some 20 of them, and their weight varies between a fraction of an ounce to 35 pounds. Until recently all of them were resting placidly in the glass cases of various museums. Among scientists they are known as the world's collection of *carbonaceous chondritic meteorites*. The earliest of them was discovered in France about 1806, and the most recent fell near an obscure village in Russia in 1961.

The carbonaceous chondrites are not the most spectacular of meteors. Usually they have been kept in the more drab rooms of the museum, where the onlookers are often disposed to glance at them briefly, shrug, and pass on. The largest is somewhat smaller than a football, and they look far more like earth-rocks than the more classical types of meteorites.

The more common stony meteorites sometimes weigh more than a ton and contain a great deal of the heavier minerals, such as iron. Indeed, possibly the major reason that we have not found more carbonaceous chondrites is that they look so much like ordinary rocks that even trained scientists have a difficult time recognizing them.

The average carbonaceous chondrite, as it enters the heavier layers of the atmosphere, creates a brilliant fireball, and all known meteorites of this type have been recovered almost immediately after impact by someone who happened to notice them coming down. They are very porous and tend to break up quickly if they are left out in the weather. More than 700 meteorites have been collected over the years, but the small percentage of these which have been carbonaceous chondrites probably does not indicate their true frequency, since these fragile space-pebbles are difficult to distinguish. In all probability, carbonaceous chondrites are quite common and abound in the small corner of space through which we pass. This fact is of considerable significance, as we shall see.

The reason for the sudden interest in these somewhat commonplace rocks is exciting indeed. The story actually began in 1834 as a result of efforts of the great Swedish chemist Jons Berzclius. A meteorite which weighed about half a pound had fallen near the little town of Alais in France in 1806. Although it had produced a brilliant ball of light on its way through the atmosphere, the small object which landed was quite undistinguished in appearance. It was about the size of a plum, and rather sooty. It had a black crust less than one-eighth of an inch thick, caused by the great heat of re-entry friction.

Inside, it appeared to be made of a clay-like earth.

Berzelius was an imaginative man, and he became excited over the possibility of examining this visitor from outer space which had arrived so spectacularly. For many years he had speculated that an analysis of meteorites might provide clues to the composition of suns and planets far removed from our own. Like all scientists, he realized that he was at an extreme disadvantage when it came to constructing any really reliable picture of the vast realm beyond this earth.

He was aware that beyond the protective miles of atmosphere he was almost blind and—in 1834—totally deaf. Except for the pitifully inadequate facts which were transmitted as visible light, he had no way of coming to grips with the great universe. Perhaps something could be learned of it through a concentrated study of meteorites, using the new tools of analytical chemistry.

As soon as he could get hold of this meteorite Berzelius addressed himself to the question of determining if it contained any materials which would indicate the presence of life on the parent body from which this small fragment had come. He soon made the exciting discovery that the Alais meteorite contained carbon compounds. The presence of carbon was considered particularly significant because scientists had always believed that carbon was found only in the remains of living things. Six years before, however, a German chemist named Friedrich Wöhler had synthesized certain carbon compounds from inorganic materials. Although Berzelius was excited by his finds, he was a disciplined and objective scientist. He was forced to decide in the end that his analysis did not justify the conclusion that "life-organisms existed in the original locality of this meteorite."

The state of chemical analysis prevented any further significant work on meteorites until about 1950. In fact, they were found to be quite difficult objects to break down chemically. The early chemists did most of their analysis by making solutions that were then allowed to react with other chemicals which produced known chemical effects. But the carbonaceous chondrites contained very little soluble material. It was not until more

110

sophisticated techniques were developed that any sustained scientific investigation of meteorites could be conducted with profit.

Early in 1953, George Mueller of London University conducted an exhaustive and more interesting study of the Cold Bakkeneld meteorite which had fallen in South Africa in 1838. Mueller and other investigators were able to show that this object contained hydrocarbons and other organic compounds. But again, the state of chemical analysis was too primitive. The precise nature of the individual materials could not be determined.

One of the largest carbonaceous chondrites is the Orgueil meteorite which fell in France in 1862. For many years this 25-pound object had been resting peacefully in the American Museum of Natural History in New York City.

In 1961 people began to be interested in meteorites again. Bartholomew Nagy and Douglas Hennessy of Fordham University, along with Warren Meinscheim of Esso Research Company, obtained a fragment of the Orgueil meteorite and subjected it to intensive study, using that relatively new and spectacular tool of modern chemistry, the mass spectrometer.

Astronomy had made use of the spectrometer since the days of Fraunhofer in the early part of the nineteenth century. Improvements have recently made it a most valuable instrument for terrestrial chemical analysis also.

The three scientists were able to report that the Orgueil meteorite contained a number of saturated hydrocarbons —carbon atoms which have the maximum number of hydrogen atoms attached to them. Such compounds are quite common in organic petroleum formed from decayed ancient plant life.

While this information was most interesting, it is doubtful that the Esso Company was unusually happy with the products of Dr. Meinscheim's labors. His employers would have certainly been more pleased if he had found indications of oil on real estate which was somewhat more accessible.

In addition, the investigators found similarities between the spectra of some of these hydrocarbons and those of

111

butter. They decided that "the mass-spectrometric analysis reveals that hydrocarbons in the Orgueil meteorite resemble in many important aspects the materials in the products of living things and sediments of life on earth. Based on these preliminary studies, the composition of the hydrocarbons in the Orgueil meteorite provides evidence of biological activity."

The chemical study of meteorites had come a long way in the century since the rather discouraging work of Berzelius.

Science has been described as "the process of self-correction," however, and it was not long before other scientists took issue with the conclusions of the three investigators. They were quick to point out that many hydrocarbons have been produced synthetically, and therefore the mere presence of such materials is not in itself sufficient proof of life origin. It has even been suggested that the radiation found in space may produce these complex hydrocarbons from inorganic chemicals.

The debate still continues, but it has been overtaken by a much more spectacular form of evidence of life on other worlds. Late in 1961, Nagy and George Claus of the New York University Medical Center made known a discovery which startled the scientific world and caused the writing of a number of somewhat wild and speculative feature stories in the Sunday newspaper supplements.

They stated that they had found microscopic-size organic particles in large quantities within the Orgueil meteorite and another object known as the Ivuna meteorite which had been found in Tanganyika in 1938. Furthermore, they felt that these objects were fossilized algae. The interest which this announcement produced was heightened by the fact that the earliest known remnant of life on earth is in the form of microscopic, single-celled algae fossils.

If the mass spectrometry experiments had raised a controversy, it was nothing to compare with the arguments that immediately began to rage over this new find. After many detailed microscopic examinations had been made, most scientists agreed that Claus and Nagy had certainly found some remarkably complex forms which could be identified only with very high magnification.

112

But were they necessarily fossil algae?

Indeed, they appeared remarkably like earth-type cell structures. Many of them had a central nucleus surrounded by a somewhat translucent bubble. They were of various sizes and shapes, and of such quantity that if they proved to be life forms, the parent body which had hurled them forth must be teeming with them.

There were three basic possibilities. They could indeed be the remains of some rudimentary space life with its origins in a distant, unknown planet which had been the victim of some long-forgotten cosmic accident. They could be a kind of unique inorganic crystal which we could not recognize because it does not exist on the earth. Or, perhaps least exciting of all, they could be a form of earthly contamination picked up from the upper layers of our own atmosphere during the turbulent passage of the meteorite on its way to earth.

Perhaps the two most remarkable characteristics of living things is that they grow and they reproduce themselves. Fredrick Sisler of the Geological Survey conducted some experiments to see if he could demonstrate the presence of these two attributes in the residue of carbonaceous chondrites. If successful, this work might help prove not only that there was other life in space, but also that it was capable of surviving the awesome hardships of a space voyage to the earth. No wonder Dr. Urey felt free to say that this was potentially the most exciting research of recent years.

Sisler placed some samples of the Murray meteorite in a germ culture medium similar to the broth used by bacteriologists. He was careful to make sure that his cultures were not contaminated by any of the local earth bacteria. Sure enough, after a few months he was able to report some growth. When it arrived at the laboratory, the meteorite definitely brought with it some living passengers. Did this mean that meteors actually carry living creatures to the earth from outer space?

Most scientists were not willing to concede that the case was proven beyond a reasonable doubt. They point out that these meteors are highly porous. Also they have been traveling for centuries in the almost perfect vacuum of space

113

and, as they enter the upper atmosphere, they "breathe in" the dust and microbes which exist at the higher levels.

Many of them have rested on the earth for some time before being picked up, and almost all of them have passed through many hands before being brought to the antiseptic and sterile haven of the laboratory. Those which have been for long periods at museums have been thrown in with all sorts of evil and exotic contamination. In fact, not only is there a strong possibility that these space visitors have picked up numerous earthly parasites, but it may also be that the many types of strange and unusual bacteria which they might be expected to carry from their earthly associations would be difficult to classify and recognize.

The scientists making these experiments have taken their samples from the center of the meteorites, but the possibility of contamination is still high. Perhaps one day a meteorite will fall through the roof of a laboratory and, although this may be hard on laboratory technicians, it will provide us with better answers than we have obtained to date.

There are other ways of determining if carbonaceous chondrites contain living organisms than attempting to grow cultures. Some scientists have examined them using the powerful magnification of the electron microscope and have found some very interesting structures indeed. Claus and Nagy have made a number of photographs of their "fossils" which show very complex particles that look like living cells. However, they cannot be identified as any specific types of life found on the earth. One investigator, Frank Staplin of the Imperial Oil Company of Canada has tentatively identified some of the organisms which he found in the Orgueil meteorite as cellular material. He also feels that it is very much like algae.

Some of the pictures that have been taken show tubular structures which remind one of plant membranes, others have spiny surfaces like cactus plants and central blobs which appear to be cell nuclei. In general, they have the appearance of rather simple forms of terrestial life.

Still, there are many skeptics among the scientific fraternity. Other investigators such as Edward Anders and Frank Fitch of the University of Chicago have compared these pictures with those of terrestrial non-life objects such as furnace ash—a compound which might be found in considerable quantity even at high altitudes. Unfortunately, as if the situation were not already confused enough, they were able to demonstrate a rather striking similarity.

One of the most exciting tests which has been applied to fragments of the meteorites has involved staining them with the same dyes that biologists use to color living tissues in order to study them under the microscope. Such stains have been used for many years by scientists to separate living tissues from the lifeless waste material which surrounds them. The stains have become a trusted test agent for living cells, since many of them change only the color of life products and do not affect inorganic matter.

Needless to say, the scientific world was extremely interested in the news that Claus and Nagy were able to color material from the Orgueil meteorite with the *Feulgen reaction* stain. This particular compound had the unique characteristic of staining a material called deoxyribonucleic acid, more popularly known as DNA. Recent experiments have shown that the chemical DNA is a vital element in the structure of living cells. Thus far it has been found only in living things, never associated with chemicals which are not the products of life tissues. If one could show that DNA was indeed present in the chondrite meteorites it would be a very powerful argument that they contained living tissues.

Again, concrete evidence eluded the frustrated scientists. The two other investigators who appear to insist on being the villains of our story, Anders and Fitch, have carried out a bit of rather discouraging research. They tried out the Feulgen reaction on three different materials: the spleen of a rat, which contains a great deal of DNA; a common rock called kimberlite; and fragments from the Orgueil meteorite.

Much to the disappointment of many scientists who were following these experiments closely, they were able to stain the inorganic kimberlite as well as the DNA-carrying spleen and the meteorite cells. After some thought, they repeated the experiment, leaving out one

115

crucial step in the process. Both the meteorite material and the kimberlite still reacted to the stain. The DNA did not.

Here then was the answer. Whatever it is that makes the material from the Orgueil meteorite react to the stain it is not DNA. As a result of this and other work it has been proven that many of the biological stains will work on non-life substances after all. It can also be argued that the intricate construction of these cells does not of itself conclusively prove that they are of life origin.

Many inorganic crystals also have complex and varied designs. Numerous examples of these can be found in the beautiful and involved patterns formed by ice crystals as they fall through the atmosphere. Comparing these with the meteorite material led Dr. Philip Morrison, then of Cornell University, to describe the meteorites as "interstellar snowflakes."

The debate still continues, and thus far the existence of extraterrestrial life has not been authenticated by the examination of the material found in meteorites. However, this flotsam from space does contain highly complex substances which have many of the properties found in simple life forms existing on the earth and the sediments from the ancient fossil beds.

The studies which have been made to date are preliminary and very limited. Who can tell what secrets may still be hidden beneath their burned and blackened surfaces? As more of the meteors are examined and our ability to analyze them improves, we may still find that they provide a major clue to the riddle of life in the universe.

The examination of meteors has confirmed one very important fact. The hydrocarbons which are found in the meteorites that have come to us from the remote vastness of space are very similar to the basic hydrocarbon building blocks which have provided the framework for life on the surface of our globe. There can be no doubt that these life materials exist on many planets among the crowded profusion of stars in our galaxy. Surely the seeds must have taken hold and grown in many other gardens besides the one which we inhabit.

Man has entered space for only a few orbits which have hugged close to his planet. But these brief moments have already propelled him into a new age, with many unknowns and great new challenges. The forces which drive us are beyond our control, and this ancient dream of the ages has now become the prime necessity of our time. No previous human endeavor has promised a greater harvest of knowledge and enrichment.

Among the questions which have intrigued our forebears since they first began to think are those involved with the great riddle of existence. Where did we come from? How did life first begin? By what process did we arrive at our present place among the stars?

When he approaches this most fascinating of all mysteries, the scientific detective is in a much poorer position than the celebrated Sherlock Holmes when he undertook the solution of his famous adventures. The deed was committed perhaps 2 billion years ago. The principals have long since died, along with all possible witnesses, and the great furnace of time has consumed all but the faintest suggestions of the scene.

As we go forward into space, we may succeed in going backward in time. One of the reasons for the great interest in searching for life on nearby planets is that a major by-product of such a search will undoubtedly be clues to the origin of life on the earth. Today, the environments of some of the other planets in our solar system are quite similar to that of earth during the formative ages of earthlife. As a result, an investigation of extra-terrestrial life will teach us a great deal about our own heritage.

One division of the National Aeronautics and Space Administration is the Exobiology Branch, which in modern terms might be translated as the Department of Far-Out Biology. The Latin root of the term literally means "life outside the earth," and this is exactly the province of the Exobiology Branch.

From the study of Mars and Jupiter we may be able to reconstruct our own past much better than by the mere examination of the faint records on this globe which nature has made available to us. Who knows, perhaps the soft waxing and waning of the green belts on Mars which have perplexed our astronomers for generations may be quite like the markings which distant observers might have seen on the earth.

The most ancient fossils are the skeletons of rudimentary algae that are very similar to those which infest our present ponds and lakes. Enough of these have been found in the ancient earth sediments, whose radioactive decay indicates a very early genealogy, to suggest that the earth must have teemed with them as long ago as 2 billion years. Recently, as we have said in an earlier chapter, some scientists believe they have found similar fossilized algae skeletons in meteorites.

Life began at a very early stage in the history of this globe. The latest estimates, based on the decay rates of radio-active materials, are probably quite accurate, and they place the birth of the earth about 4.5 billion years ago. Life began spontaneously a remarkably short time later—not less than 4.2 billion years ago. We do not know anything about this first life, but algae are relatively complex forms and the first living organisms were probably much more simple. We haven't found any of them yet.

We do know that the earth's atmosphere has gone through a considerable change since that early time, and a large part of the atmospheric evolution has been caused by the life of the planet, as though life has the power to tailor the air to meet its requirements and produce the best medium for its requirements.

The larger planets, Jupiter and Saturn, have retained considerable quantities of the lighter gases such as hydrogen and helium even to modern times because of their strong gravitational attraction. Atmospheres of the smaller planets tend to be composed of the heavier gases —oxygen, nitrogen, and carbon dioxide—which are nourishing to life.

In the beginning, the atmospheres of the planets were probably quite similar. All of them included such gases as hydrogen, ammonia, and methane. Later, as in the case of the earth, when the crusts of the planets cooled, many of the gases found in the rocks slowly escaped into the air. These were mainly oxygen, carbon dioxide, and water vapor. The formation of the original vast quantity of oxygen which is present in our atmosphere today is still something of a mystery. There is no doubt, however, that once plants began to grow they exhaled oxygen to increase the available supply.

Life almost certainly began during the early stages of earth development, when the atmosphere was quite like that of Jupiter today. Scientists have already been able to create in the laboratory some of the complex molecules which are the building blocks of life by simulating the earth's atmosphere. Once the fire was kindled and the first feeble flames began to flicker, the vast accretion of life required only time. Certain errors which occurred in the repetition of the chemical combinations, together with the mutations produced by radiation, began to mold and shape the early life molecules into a myriad of different forms. The process of biological evolution was firmly launched. Ultimately, it would produce *homo sapiens* himself.

We know that this development took place on earth, and the odds are good that something similar has also happened on one or more of the other planets in our solar system. No doubt it has occurred many times among the millions of planets of other stars in our galaxy.

Locally, Mars was long thought to be the most likely candidate. Indeed, the seasonal changes noted on the Martian surface, as well as the presence of carbon dioxide and water vapor in the Martian atmosphere, are indications of the possibility of life on the surface of our nearest neighbor.

Atmosphere alone, however, is not enough. The temperature must lie within relatively narrow limits. Mercury is very close to the sun, and is probably much too hot to allow the existence of the soft, jelly-like life with which we are familiar. The temperature of Venus has been the source of some recent controversy.

The highly publicized results of the Mariner II flight, for example, indicated that the surface of Venus burned with unmerciful heat, at a temperature of 430° C. while even the outer clouds were 94° C. Only a few months later quite different results were published by Dr. John Strong of Johns Hopkins University.

Dr. Strong obtained his data from a balloon-borne telescope lifted to an altitude of only 16 miles. However, this was high enough to obtain some very interesting and controversial results, even though it did not compare with the spectacular flight of NASA's Mariner II, which journeyed to within 21,000 miles of the planet and radioed back a vast number of measurements.

The most important data obtained by Dr. Strong's observatory, which incidentally cost the sponsoring U.S. Air Force only $100,000, was derived from scanning the infrared rays from the sun after they had been reflected by the Venusian clouds. Following a careful analysis of his data, Dr. Strong was able to plot an accurate curve of these infrared reflections. The curve did not agree at all with the corresponding reflection curves for dust, carbon dioxide, liquid formaldehyde, and other substances which were thought to make up the noxious clouds of the Venusian atmosphere.

Dr. Strong's curve matched almost perfectly the reflection spectrum of an ice-crystal cloud produced in his laboratory. Since the earth's high clouds are also formed of ice crystals, this find has re-opened the question of life on Venus, which was thought to have been settled forever by the results of Mariner II. Since the ice-crystal clouds reflect a large portion of the sun's heat, the unseen surface of Venus may be relatively cool, perhaps almost as cool as the surface of the earth. The Millstone Hill radar center at M.I.T.'s Lincoln Laboratory, recently confirmed Dr. Strong's findings. Scientists at the lab have discovered evidence that the atmosphere of Venus absorbs radio waves at the characteristic wave length of water vapor, 3 centimeters.

In addition, Dr. Strong has advanced some arguments which cast suspicion on the methods used in the space-probe experiments to measure planetary surface temperatures based on the emission of radio waves. Dr. Strong contends that other factors besides high surface temperatures may generate these waves. As all aviators know from the static in their receivers, turbulent clouds radiate large amounts of radio energy.

The spectacular photographs of the red planet Mars transmitted back to earth by Mariner IV reveal a surface which is more moon-like than earth-like. The stark features of our nearest planetary neighbor display little evidence of erosion. Hence it is unlikely that the planet has been exposed to large amounts of water vapor or atmosphere during its recent history. This would surely make the evolution of life more difficult, but it is not conclusive evidence. In order to determine whether or not the fragile chemical delicacy which clings so tenaciously to our earth has established a beachhead on Mars, we must land instruments. Pictures are not enough.

The climate of Mars is harsh, but perhaps not impossible for life. There is a growing body of evidence that some forms of life do exist on Mars, and most scientists will be surprised if the devices which are now being built by the National Aeronautics and Space Administration do not demonstrate the existence of Martian life.

Jupiter, Saturn, Uranus, Neptune, and Pluto are generally considered to be too cold for life. But are they really?

Actually the atmospheric conditions of Jupiter are much similar to those of the young earth. Quite probably there is a wide range of temperatures between the surface of the planet and the outer layers of atmosphere. We know that the "greenhouse effect" of the earth traps and holds a good deal of the sun's heat. Couldn't the same sort of thing be happening today in the Jovian atmosphere?

Indeed, if we regard the origin of life as the central mystery in an interstellar detective story, then the deed and the scene may be in the process of being duplicated in several places in our own solar system. By sending probes, then robots, and finally scientists to our nearest neighbors we should be able to find out how it really began for us.

In addition to sea and land life, we may find complex

forms living in the atmospheres of some planets. There is considerable evidence that life first began in the air of our own planet.

During the next few years, the program which NASA has undertaken offers a great deal of promise for solving many of the perplexities of our solar system. The probes which have been launched toward the moon, Venus, and Mars are the mere forerunners of much more complicated and advanced projects which are now in the design stage.

By far the most interesting and exciting of our neighbors for these scientists is the planet Mars. For the past 100 years men have speculated on the possibilities of life on this planet which is next outside the earth from the sun. Percival Lowell constructed his observatory at Flagstaff, Arizona, and installed in it one of the finest telescopes ever built by the great lens-maker Alvin Clark in order to solve the mystery of life on Mars. Many other scientists have devoted much of their lives to research on the habitability of Mars. To date this work is inconclusive, but the evidence points strongly toward the existence of some sort of organic activity.

Mars is on the average 141 million miles from the sun, while the earth is only 93 million miles away. The Martian year is 687 earth-days long. At their closest approach, which is called *favorable opposition* by astronomers, the earth and Mars are usually about 50 million miles apart, although they can be as close as 34 million miles.

The period of closest approach occurs about every 26 months, and it is at these times that the astronomers train their telescopes on the red planet. This is also the time when space probes and manned voyages to Mars must be launched. At other times Mars and the earth can be as far apart as 240 million miles, with the sun between them, a rather difficult position for both the astronomer and the astronaut. The optimum time for launching rockets to intercept or pass close to Mars is three or four months before the date of closest approach.

The Mariner probes were not scheduled to land on the planet, but to pass nearby at a range of about 10,000 miles. They were designed to carry instrumentation to obtain a great wealth of data on planetary phenomena. High-quality television photographs of the planet can be made from this distance, along with readings of the infrared spectrum. The read-back of all this data is done by radio signals from the rocket similar to those of Mariner II.

On November 28, 1964, the Mariner IV spacecraft was launched from Cape Kennedy on its way to one of the most spectacular voyages ever made. United States scientists waited anxiously through the following months while adjustments corrected its course and tests were conducted to verify the state of its complicated mechanism. A minor failure in a key part, the strike of a wandering meteorite, any one of a thousand mishaps and the months of planning and effort would have gone for nothing. Dr. William Pickering, the director of California's Jet Propulsion Laboratory, and his crew of Mariner scientists did not breathe easily until July 15, 1965, when the first pictures began to flash back over the millions of space miles which separate us from our nearest planetary neighbor.

In all, 22 precious photographs were radioed back to earth. They must surely be ranked among the highest achievements of all our scientific history. A number of other experiments, such as the measurement of trapped radiation in the vicinity of Mars, estimates of the height of the Martian atmosphere, and measurements of the magnetic field were also accomplished. Mariner IV radioed a total of more than 260 million bits of data back to her earth-bound masters 134 million miles away —a truly incredible performance.

What does all this data mean in terms of the probability of finding life on Mars?

A total of 70 craters are clearly distinguishable on Mariner IV photos five through 15, and they range in diameter from 3 to 75 miles. There are doubtless many smaller craters which could not be seen in the Mariner IV pictures. In addition, since the photos covered only about one per cent of the Martian surface, it is not unlikely that there are also many larger ones.

The rims of the Martian craters appear to rise several hundred feet above the surrounding surface. In general,

123

they slope upward at rather steep angles; some of them are quite new while others appear to be old. The numbers seen would indicate that the surface is less pock-marked than the densely cratered uplands of the moon.

The photos definitely show that the surface of Mars is more like that of the moon than that of the earth. The clear definition of the Martian craters indicates that Mars has been without a significant atmosphere since the craters were formed. In addition, it is hard to visualize the presence of any large quantity of surface water since that time; otherwise the craters would be blurred by erosion.

Stress and deformation produced by upheaval within the earth have produced most of its topographical features, but this is not true of Mars. There are few indications of mountains and valleys, no oceans or rivers, and internally the planet must have been inactive for many ages. In addition, the occultation experiment conducted when Mariner IV disappeared temporarily behind the planetary disk, indicates that the Martian atmosphere is less than one per cent as dense as the earth's.

The seemingly barren surface of Mars caused many scientists to believe that the possibility of life on that planet was considerably diminished. To be sure, the search for fossils and other skeletal life remnants does appear to be less promising if oceans never existed on Mars and the planet has been without atmosphere through all ages.

But is this necessarily so? After detailed study of the Mariner IV pictures, not all scientists agree that Mars has been forever a barren and dead world.

The Martian and the lunar craters are thought to be caused by the impact of two types of objects, comets and asteroids of the Apollo group whose orbits cross those of Earth and Mars. Scientists who have made a study of the bombardment rates of these wanderers feel that the frequency of impacts should be several times greater on Mars than the number of craters indicates, if it has been exposed to these projectiles as long as the moon has. It would appear that the relative density of craters on Mars in comparison to those of the moon is about a ratio of 1 to 6. Scientists believe this may mean that Martian craters have resulted from meteorite impacts which have occurred only during the past 300 to 700 million years. Prior to that time, perhaps Mars was surrounded by a relatively dense atmosphere which, like that of the earth, caused the meteorites to burn up prior to reaching the surface. It may be that Mars had such a protective atmosphere during the first 3.5 million years of development.

It has also been pointed out by Carl Sagan that Mariner IV would have found no evidence of life on the earth had it passed by 6,000 miles distant, as it did from Mars. Sagan examined a number of the weather pictures taken by the Tiros Nimbus satellites. Although these were photographed only a few hundred miles from the surface and have somewhat better resolution than the Mariner IV pictures, which fail to show detail smaller than 3 miles in diameter, he could find no hint of our cities, highways, or farms. Even the signs of the earth's vegetation, and the shading produced by the changing seasons were extremely difficult to detect. Sagan concluded that the Mariner IV photos neither prove nor disprove the possibility of life on Mars.

Astronomer Clyde Tombaugh, the discoverer of Pluto, noted that several of the markings on Mariner IV pictures coincide with the canals and the oasis which have been mapped by many astronomers since the time of Schiaparelli. He found that one of the largest craters is located where astronomers have long thought there was an oasis. Faint lines running from the bottom of this crater are in the same position as a canal first drawn by Percival Lowell in 1894.

Tombaugh and other astronomers have speculated that the canals may be cracks or fissures in the Martian surface. Perhaps vegetation in the form of hardy lichens and moss capable of withstanding the harsh Martian climate inhabit these cracks which are warmed by the hot gases from inside the planet. The waxing and waning of this growth may produce the apparent changes in the Martian seasons.

As good as they are, the Mariner IV pictures are not enough. It will take other voyages even more spectacular to settle finally the debate regarding life on Mars. Soft landings such as those which the U.S. and Russia are now making on the moon, coupled with carefully controlled experiments, will ultimately provide a conclusive answer. Soon after that, man will go and see for himself.

The instruments contained in the exploration package of the first Mariner launched to search for life on Mars will be soft-landed on the surface, and no attempt will be made to bring them back to earth, at least not initially.

What sort of instruments are these?

Actually there are quite a number and variety of them. A few of those which NASA scientists are currently working on are the following: the Wolf Trap, Optical Rotary Dispersion Profile Indicator, Multivator, Vidicon Microscope, J-Band Life Detector, Radioisotope Biochemical Probe, Mass Spectrometer, and Ultraviolet Spectrophotometer. It is interesting to look at each of these briefly in order to see what NASA expects to search for on the Martian surface.

According to NASA scientists, "When Professor Wolf Vishniac conceived his search for life in space device, he called it the bug detector. It was inevitable, however, that his biologist friends would rename it the *Wolf Trap*." The Wolf Trap is a device for detecting the presence of life on whatever surface it falls upon, by means of placing samples of the local soil in culture tubes. The growth of whatever bacteria these samples contain is then sensed by the Wolf Trap.

Professor Vishniac's device is quite unlike anything used by the trappers of the past. It consists of a long, tightly sealed cylinder which has a small, fragile tube running along one side. The tube has one end made of glass or some other frangible material, and this extends slightly below the bottom of the cylinder so that it will strike the surface of whatever spot the device comes to rest on first.

The other end of the tube pierces the side of the cylinder near the top and leads into a hollow tube running down through the center of the Wolf Trap. This inner tube has most of the air exhausted, so that it is almost a vacuum, with a pressure lower than that of the surrounding atmosphere, even that of Mars. The lower portion of the tube will contain a culture medium similar to that used by biologists to grow bacteria on the earth. There will be photoelectric cells in the tube as well as electrodes, and the Wolf Trap will contain a radio to transmit its infomation back to earth.

The Wolf Trap works as follows. The complete package will be lowered quite gently to the surface of Mars perhaps by a parachute. We must know a good deal more about the atmosphere of Mars than we do now, however, if we are to design such a parachute to bring its fragile and complicated load to rest without a nasty bump which might upset the mechanism. As the Wolf Trap touches the surface, its outside tube strikes the ground first and the lower end shatters. The vacuum inside the cylinder will then suck the unknown dust of its resting place into the interior of the Wolf Trap.

If there are bacteria present similar to those of the earth, some of them are almost sure to come to rest in the culture medium, and some of that portion may catch hold, grow, and multiply. As soon as the Wolf Trap has inhaled a quantity of the local atmosphere, dust, and— it is hoped—living organisms proportionally equal to the outside air pressure, the opening of the trap will be closed by a spring-loaded valve. "This," according to Professor Vishniac, "will prevent evaporation of the culture medium and any possible contamination of the planetary surface by the terrestrial organic matter which may be inside."

At first there will be no signs of life and the radio can only report that the Wolf Trap has performed its various functions in the proper manner. If bacteria are present and if they begin to grow, there will ultimately be two effects which can be measured and transmitted back to earth. First, the culture medium will change color and become slowly clouded by the extraterrestrial growth. This color change will be sensed by the photoelectric cells. Secondly, the acidity of the medium will probably change, because all life forms of which we are aware contain acids in their nuclei. This nucleonic acid will change the electrical conductivity of the medium and small electrodes will measure this change so that it can be transmitted back to earth.

Professor Vishniac says: "The principle of the Wolf

Trap is susceptible to a variety of modifications. The first device will be as simple as possible. After the successful construction of the first model, we can elaborate on it. First, varied media may be provided to search for different types of microorganisms, including photosynthetic bacteria.

"Second, the response of the signalling device could be changed from a simple yes-no answer capability to a more complex response. The change in turbidity as a result of bacterial growth, which will result in a change in light intensity registered by the photocell, could be coupled to a change in frequency in the signalling device.

"The variation in this signal, then, would be a measure of the rate of growth of the bacteria. From this it would be possible to plot a growth curve. Similarly, a change of acidity might be signalled by the electrode in terms of rate of change—rather than a simple yes-no signal."

As with any man-made trap, this one is not foolproof. There will be no way of controlling the exact spot where the Wolf Trap will land, and it may come to rest on some barren rock where no life exists. In such a case, an erroneous negative answer may come back.

Professor Vishniac himself has said that the signal may possibly show a marked change in the culture medium right after impact. This would prove only that Mars has a very dusty surface and that the dust contains a great deal of acid.

If no change at all is noted in the medium, this does not necessarily mean that no life was drawn into the Wolf Trap. It would merely indicate that no life is present which will live in the sort of bacteria broth upon which earth bacteria thrive.

The ideal finding, of course, would be one where there is an initial period of quiet followed by slow changes in the electrical potential and the translucence of the medium. This would be an excellent indication that life has been discovered on Mars.

Identification of life by means of Optical Rotary Dispersion Profiles makes use of new techniques which will first be tried on meteorite samples. The same techniques will then be applied to the material of other planets when it becomes available. The experiments will be designed to answer two questions: What is life? How do you know when you have found it?

Dr. Ira Blei is the NASA scientist who is in charge of the optical rotation experiments. He says: "The answer to these questions brings us to the heart of the problem of the search for life on other planets. We must discover how to design single experiments which will provide enough information to permit a decision to be made concerning the existence of extraterrestrial life.

"Life has become very difficult to define in just a few words. The highest form of life on earth, man, is a collection of very complex molecules having certain life-like properties associated with them.

"At the other end of the scale are many types of simple chemical substances such as sugars which are obviously not alive but are yet closely related to life and exhibit some life characteristics. Further, somewhere between the two extremes, molecules exist which are sometimes alive and sometimes unalive—the viruses.

"So we must look for a property which is common to all things we would be willing to call living. This substance appears to be deoxyribonucleic acid, or DNA. It is apparently the key molecule which contains the coded heritable information passed on from one generation to the next—from the lowest forms of life up to man. If we find DNA on another planet through this experiment, we can accept this as evidence that life exists there."

Through an electron microscope, DNA appears like a long string of pearls. It is, in fact, a large molecule made up of many lesser molecules. Such large aggregations of molecules are called polymers. DNA has a property common to many complex molecules which tend to absorb portions of the ultraviolet spectrum. By measuring the amount of this absorption, we may be able to identify these substances in the same way that a modern police department can identify suspects by their fingerprints. If there is such a fingerprint for DNA, it may provide a sure way of identifying life wherever we find it.

However, there are problems. The particular absorption of DNA is a characteristic of its base chemical adenine. For a long time it was thought that adenine could be associated only with life products, just as it was once felt that hydrocarbons were strictly life substances. Unfortunately, the true essence of living things turns out to be much more elusive. Adenine has recently been synthesized spontaneously in artificial systems which contain no life. Therefore the identification of adenine ultraviolet absorption is not enough.

Fortunately we have been able to isolate another characteristic of DNA. The sugar which DNA contains is capable of rotating a shaft of polarized light. This rotation of a polarized beam causes it to be seen in a different plane from before, and is quite easy to measure.

These two unique characteristics when found together allow us to be reasonably certain that the vital life substance DNA is present. Dr. Blei is presently designing experiments to measure these characteristics in substances from other planets.

The Multivator Life Detection System is being developed at Stanford University Medical Center by Nobel Prize winner Dr. Joshua Lederberg. It is one of the smallest gadgets under development for its purpose and can be carried as a part of the payload on a Mariner space probe.

Without its battery power supply and the sample collector which will feed it the material to be tested, the Multivator weighs only one pound. It is just over 2 inches in diameter and about 10 inches long, just a bit larger than a tube of frozen ready-mix biscuits.

Despite its small size, the Multivator is designed to perform a number of precisely controlled studies under conditions similar to those found in the best laboratories. These experiments will have objectives similar to those of the Wolf Trap, since they are designed to determine the presence of bacteria in the soil of a planet. The scientists who are developing the Multivator believe that once the seed of life begins to germinate on a planet it very quickly permeates the entire surface, so that soon it can be found in almost any drop of water, any pinch of soil, or for that matter, any gust of wind. Like the Wolf Trap, the results of Multivator experiments will be radioed back to earth.

How will the Multivator work?

It must first be parachuted to the surface of the planet

with reasonable care in order not to damage the sensitive instrumentation. Dust will be sucked through the inlet channel into a total of 15 different chambers where experiments will be conducted. A viscous adhesive material on the walls of the chambers will collect the dust, and the chamber openings will then be automatically sealed off.

The initial Multivator experiments will be designed to detect enzymes, another one of the vital classes of chemicals which are associated with living things. The presence of certain enzymes causes reactions in other chemicals, which can be measured and recorded by the instruments. For example, one enzyme, called phosphatase, breaks down phosphates which are required by living things. The phosphates can be made to change color when broken down by the phosphatase, and this color change can be measured by the Multivator.

Since many experiments can be performed simultaneously by this device, they can be designed in such a way that they complement each other. In this way the Multivator can be used to build up a considerable case for or against the existence of life on any planet which it reaches.

Dr. Lederberg is also designing a second device for detecting life on Mars, and in many ways this is the most exciting of all the present group of projects, because it offers promise of allowing us to see the life which may exist on a neighboring planet. The Vidicon Microscope, as it is called, is quite similar to an ordinary microscope except that it has a television camera attached to the eye end. This camera further magnifies the image produced by the microscope and will allow it to be transmitted back to earth.

Not only can such a microscope be used to search for life, but it will also help us to learn something about soil and the structure of the planetary surface. Dr. Lederberg has estimated that such a microscope can be constructed with the amazingly low weight of 3 pounds.

The J-Band Life Detector and mass spectrometer are two devices which will be able to detect the presence of certain chemical combinations on the Martian surface. The J-Band Detector will search for proteins, and the mass spectrometer will look for the complex amino acids which are among the basic building blocks of living things. In addition, it will be able to investigate other complicated chemical structures. Dr. Freeman Quimby, Chief of Exobiology at NASA, has stated that the mass spectrometer may be able to detect forms of life which are unknown on the earth.

One of the most interesting of the experiments which are being developed to search for life on Mars was developed from experiments that were first employed to test drinking water. This project is appropriately named Gulliver, and is the result of the efforts of two enterprising young NASA scientists, Dr. Gilbert Levin and Dr. Norman Horwitz.

Normally, biologists expect that it will take a minimum of 48 hours for bacteria from drinking water to begin growing when samples are placed in a culture medium. However, Dr. Levin found that this process is speeded up many times when the culture broth has been treated with radioisotopes so that it is slightly radioactive. Under these conditions bacteria will give evidence of their growth in four hours or less.

Gulliver will contain such a broth, which has been "tagged" with radioisotopes. This broth must be carefully sterilized so that the scientists are certain that it contains no living cells when it leaves the earth. Material from Mars will be fed into the broth after Gulliver has completed its voyage to the planet. If living organisms begin to multiply in the broth, they will produce a radioactive gas which will activate a Geiger counter. The frequency of the clicks produced by the Geiger counter will indicate the speed of growth of the bacteria, and this information will be recorded and transmitted back to earth.

Gulliver has another interesting feature. In a limited sense, it is capable of hunting for its own samples. Three 50-foot spools of line will be installed inside the device and these are to be coated with a viscous adhesive. After Gulliver lands on Mars, small windows will open in the capsule wall so that miniature cannons can fire projectiles through these ports. Attached to each will be one of the lines. When the string is fully extended, a small motor begins to reel them in and the sticky coating picks up samples of soil and perhaps vegetation, which is drawn into the body of the device.

After all the lines are in, Gulliver seals itself off from the outside world and begins to examine its find. First the string is allowed to soak in the radio-active culture broth. If life is present, the Geiger counter will soon begin to click, and the news will be signalled back to earth.

A first model of Gulliver has already been built and tested in Rock Creek Park in Washington, D.C., not far from NASA Headquarters. On the first test, one of the projectiles snagged on the limb of a tree, but the experiment was still successful. Bacteria growth was recorded by the Geiger counter within an hour.

Gulliver actually resembles one of the Lilliputians more than it does its namesake. The current design weighs less than one pound and is just over 6 inches high.

None of the early experimental packages which are landed on Mars will transmit directly back to earth, but will do so via relay through a satellite which will remain in orbit around Mars after the instrument capsules have been dropped to the surface. This mother satellite is called a "bus," and after it has carried its precious load to the vicinity of Mars it will become a relay transmitter for all the information that the robots are able to obtain about life on the planet.

These are only the first of many experiments to come in the quest for life in our solar system. NASA has published an advertisement in the Bulletin of the American Institute for Biological Sciences which calls for more experiments in the search for extraterrestrial life. Some of NASA's interests are: "Exobiology Program. Ground-based and in-flight experiments to identify and study extraterrestrial life and determine the type of analysis necessary for such identification. Analysis and development of space probe decontamination methods, ground-based research on the origin of organic compounds, analysis of meteorites for organic constituents, distribution and characterization of microbes in the upper terrestrial atmosphere, infrared spectroscopic analysis of the planets, and the design and flight of experiments for the detection and study of life on other planets."

It will not be long before Wolf Traps, crawling Gulliver bugs, and other devices will be located on every planet in our solar system. The biologists have become as interested in the space programs as are the astronomers. They are beginning to realize that the best way to answer basic questions about the riddle of existence on the earth is to search out the secrets of life on other planets.

14 | ECONOMY CLASS TO THE MOON

In a few years man will have his robots, Gullivers, Wolf Traps, and other devices generously sprinkled throughout the solar system. They will radio back a continuous electronic chronicle about the universe, about the beginning of life, and about the evolutionary staircase. They will usher in a great new era of discovery, bringing untold riches, similar to the age of Columbus and the explorers who came after him.

There will be many "soft" landings by unmanned spaceships such as that accomplished by Luna 9, the Russian craft which first survived impact with the lunar surface after four previous unsuccessful attempts. These also will tell us a great deal about our natural satellites.

But all of this will not be enough. Man will want to go and see for himself. The first attempt by Americans to visit extraterrestrial soil will occur, if all goes well, before 1970 as a result of the much publicized Apollo Program for which astronauts are already in training and the rockets are already being constructed.

The preparation for this first epic voyage to the moon already employs 300,000 workers of more than 20,000 separate companies. In the fiscal year ending July 1, 1966 alone, the manned flight program carried a price tag of $3.5 billion.

The Gargantuan industrial complex which is devoted to space flight is already twice as large as the automobile industry and employs 1.5 million people—over 2 per cent of the total labor force of the country. The annual cost is correspondingly astronomical—more than $20 billion per year. This great octopus which has tentacles reaching into all the major segments of American business is all the more amazing because it did not even exist before the mid-1950's.

First, and perhaps most important, of the moon industry products is Saturn V, the huge silver needle which will one day roar skyward toward the moon and planets, as the world breathlessly waits below. Measuring 370 feet, Saturn is taller than all but the major skyscrapers in our largest cities. It will be 35 feet in diameter at its base, and will weigh more than 3,000 tons—more than a modern destroyer.

The great engines, five of them in the first stage, will burn fuel at the rate of 1.5 million pounds per minute. During their 2½ minute life span they will consume enough liquid to fill more than 50 railroad tank cars. As soon as this mighty first effort is completed, at less than 40 miles above the earth, this gigantic first stage will be shucked off to fall back into the Atlantic, and the five smaller engines of the second stage will begin their work.

Altogether, three stages will be required to propel the first spacemen to the moon. Only one stage is needed to bring them back, because of the much greater gravitational pull of the earth. The three crewmen will have to pilot their craft through the uncharted blackness of space by means of fixes and bearings on the earth and the distant stars. They will be tracked closely by earth-bound radars, and scientists will be able to tell them immediately if they stray off course.

The astronauts will have plenty to do in addition to their navigational chores during the 2½ day lunar journey. When they reach the moon's vicinity, they must perform the extremely delicate and precise job of rotating Apollo to a tail-first position in order to slow down their space ship. This is required to position Apollo in a lunar orbit. Otherwise, because of the great energy needed to escape the shackles of the earth's gravity, it would pass the moon at high speed and continue into space, ultimately establishing itself as a private, three-man planet in orbit around the sun.

An orbit at an altitude of 100 miles will be established

around the moon by the Apollo's command and service module. This is the basic or "space ship" unit of the Apollo system. At this point, two of the astronauts will climb into the lunar excursion module, called the LEM, and be separated from the command and service module for the trip to the moon's surface. Braking rockets will slow the LEM's descent. At the last moment, the astronauts can cause their craft to hover over the landing area at an altitude of about 300 feet. If they do not like what they can see of the surface below, they can return to the mother ship without landing. However, this must be regarded as an extremely unlikely event if astronauts are anything like the explorers of old.

The LEM will have windows which allow the astronauts to study the lunar surface from the safety of their craft before venturing forth. They will be able to move the LEM from one position to another in the landing area in order to pick the best spot. The landing speed will be less than 7 miles per hour, just fast enough to provide a slight bump as the LEM comes to rest. The command module, carrying the remaining astronaut, will have an orbit timed so that it is directly overhead during the landing sequence.

Once they have landed on the moon, the astronauts will not be satisfied to view its parched, cracked surface only from the safety of their vehicle. Just like Columbus and his crew, they will want to step ashore on the beaches of this unknown new world. They will have moon landing suits for this purpose, and as soon as they have made certain that their frail craft has made its voyage intact and is in shape for the trip back to earth, one of them will step out on the moon's surface and explore the area around the LEM.

What a unique historical occasion this moment will be! After the long millenniums of being shackled by gravity and distance to his earthly prison, man will have truly broken the old fetters which bound him. This first moon explorer will be the product of a few short years of extraordinary progress. In considerably less than one century, man will have proceeded from not being able to fly at all, to flight in air, to orbital flight, and then to a trip to the moon. No past age has brought so rapid a fulfillment of our ancient dreams.

If all goes well, this first astronaut will remain outside his space ship for about four hours. Moon gravity is only one-sixth that of the earth, so it will take him a little time to learn how to get about. If he weighs 180 pounds on earth, he will only weigh 30 pounds on the moon. In later years this may make the moon a very popular vacation spot for fat people who are tired of lugging their excess avoirdupois around on the earth.

The first astronaut will take pictures of the lunar surface and carefully collect samples of the lunar soil. He will also plant the American flag, and will begin a number of experiments which will be completed later by his successors.

After 4 hours he will return to the LEM and his partner will have a chance to explore the moon's surface. The first LEM will remain on the moon for perhaps one 24-hour earth-day. Now that man has moved outward to other bodies in the solar system, he must qualify some of his measuring sticks. It will no longer be sufficient to say one day or one hour, we will have to speak in terms of Martian days or Jovian hours. A lunar day, for example, is almost as long as an earth-month.

The LEM will blast off the moon at a moment when the command module, containing the envious third astronaut, is just coming up over the horizon. The 3,000-pound-thrust engine will burn for about 6 minutes, which will be long enough to put the craft in orbit at a speed of about 4,000 miles per hour. The two space craft will coast about halfway around the moon, at which time they should be quite close together. The relative difference in their speeds will be less than 100 miles per hour, and the delicate, precise maneuver of docking the LEM will now begin.

Once the LEM has delivered its passengers to the command module, it will be detached from the mother vehicle and "parked" in a lunar orbit. After paying the cost in weight and energy to send it to the moon it would be foolish to bring such a valuable moon satellite back to earth again. There will be other astronauts and other moon flights. This first LEM will surely be useful to them.

The command-module engines will be re-ignited and the 2½ day journey back to earth will begin for the triumphant astronauts. The final descent will be by parachute as the command module is brought gently to earth through the lower atmosphere.

More sophisticated lunar exploration flights will be undertaken later. No doubt, by the end of this century, humans will have spent as much time on the moon as they have now spent in earth orbits. The future moon stations may ultimately become self-sustaining, nurtured by fuels found in the lunar rocks and by the universal heat of the sun. Even if they must be fed from the earth, scientists estimate that such stations ultimately will not cost more than $1,000,000 per man per year to keep going.

Even though it does not now appear possible for man to visit the planets of other stars, he will surely explore all those of the sun. The first of these exploratory flights beyond the orbit of the moon will be conducted before the end of this century, so that by the year 2,000 humans will have landed on Mars and perhaps on one or more of the other planets.

One of the major problems associated with such travel will be that of obtaining fuel for the voyages. No find of greater importance to the future of exploration would be possible than the discovery of suitable rocket fuels on the moon. A lunar service station which could fill up the tanks of both earth-bound and outbound space ships would be of incalculable value, since it would be located on such a low gravity platform and thus would be well along on the road to the cosmos. The vast quantities of energy required to allow the most humble of space craft to escape the great pull of the earth could be replaced during the outbound journey by fuel which would then become available for the trip to Mars or beyond.

Although the great explorers of old made their journeys in search of gold or eternal youth, the modern adventurers will proceed outward on much less romantic quests—at least at first. Their primary objective will be to find fuel for even more ambitious flights.

If we succeed in making the moon a way-station on the road to exploration of the planets, this will have side effects of almost equal importance. A lunar astronomical observatory, for example, might have far more power and other resources available than one placed in orbit around the earth. It would have most of the advantages of a satellite observatory, since it would not be surrounded by a blurring and filtering atmosphere, and the distortion of its instruments by lunar gravity would be much less than the gravitational warping of earth-bound equipment.

A lunar radio astronomy complex might even be more useful, chiefly because of the large quantities of power such a station needs to communicate with the planets of other stars. Once a lunar station is fully established, it will certainly contain vast power plants, nuclear as well as conventional. By the time humans have developed such a station on the moon, they should be able and willing to spend a portion of their resources in contacting the intelligent citizens of other planets.

There are a number of problems which face the first explorers of even our nearest neighbor, Mars. The red planet can only be approached from the earth during about 2 months out of every 26. During the remaining time, Mars is too remote from the earth for economical space flight. Even under the optimum conditions, a flight to Mars will require at least 6 months. This must be followed by a wait of more than a year before the return journey can be attempted, again because of the relative position of the two planets. Because of the long flight time and the waiting period, a Mars flight is a formidable enterprise indeed. In addition to the vast amount of fuel required for the trip, the explorers must be able to sustain themselves for this long period in an alien environment. The stories told by our first Martian explorers on their return will surely rival the offerings of our most imaginative science-fiction writers.

But no matter. The time is not too long and the trip is not too hard. Magellan's crew took 3 years to circumnavigate the earth, and before the voyage was completed more than half were dead. Man can fly to Mars and he will demonstrate this fact before the end of the century. Because of the dynamic progress of human knowledge, fewer lives will be lost than during the early days of ocean exploration.

Many scientists are now convinced that the chances

are good that we will discover some sort of life on Mars despite its barren surface and harsh climate. Almost everyone who has studied the problem feels that tough and hardy plants similar to those of the earth's deserts could live on Mars, and even the possibility of some sort of animal life is not entirely discounted.

The Philco Corporation's scientists recently made a study for NASA to forecast what the first Mars explorers might find. They said: "In the event higher animal forms are encountered, it will be desirable to trap living specimens. They will probably be hard to capture, and photographs or casts of surface imprints may have to suffice."

The moon can provide a record billions of years old, uneroded by water or atmosphere, of the development of our chemical origin. The very first visit may finally end the controversy as to whether the solar system was formed by explosion or condensation. If we condensed instead of exploded into being, the chances will be much better that there are others like us in the universe. The exploration of Mars may provide an equally revealing record of our biological development. The new explorers will not only push outward the old physical boundaries which have constricted us through all past time, but they will also widen the more important boundaries within our minds.

Near the end of the last century Simon Newcomb, a famous mathematician of the period, stated that the moon was a world on which nothing ever happened. Like the author of many another scientific generality, almost immediately he found himself involved in a rather heated debate.

At almost the same time, a unique and somewhat bizarre theory was being advanced by a Danish mathematician named Peter Hansen, who had been attempting to calculate the precise period of the orbit of the moon. Try as he would, he could not get the actual period to coincide with his predicted one.

Peter Hansen finally decided that his difficulties stemmed from the fact that the moon is not round, that it bulges, in fact, in the direction of the earth. He postulated that the moon is almost football-shaped, with one of the pointed ends always facing in our direction. The far side of the moon, said Hansen, might not resemble the part we see at all. He believed it was quite possible that there was water, air, plants, and—who knows?—even people hidden behind the enigmatic surface which faces us.

Who said nothing ever happens on the moon?

Needless to say, Simon Newcomb became interested in Hansen's theory and undertook a detailed study of the moon's surface, which had two primary results. First, Newcomb was able to prove by mathematical analysis that Hansen could not possibly be right with his football-shaped view of our only natural satellite. Secondly, Newcomb established himself as the foremost authority of the day on things lunar.

Even so, his statement that nothing ever happens on the surface of the moon turned out to be something less than the last word.

Actually, there were those who had suspected that changes took place on the moon's surface long before this famous controversy. A highly respected German astronomer named Jules Schmidt announced in 1866 that he had detected a change in a small crater called Linne, after the famous Swedish naturalist. This object was described on two authoritative maps as being about 6 miles across and quite deep. According to his announcement in 1866, Schmidt found that the crater had disappeared and that the surface at that spot was actually elevated slightly from the surrounding region. He went on to say that previous observations of the region, made before 1850, had indicated a crater similar to that described in these moon maps.

Unfortunately, all this took place before the use of photographic plates, and before the telescopes which in recent years have been able to settle such disputes quickly and conclusively. Therefore, it cannot be proved conclusively that such a change did take place. There can be no doubt, however, that Linne today is a small plateau, not a crater.

There have been other attempts to verify the existence of change on the moon's surface. During World War II, several scientists whose normal work had been interrupted by the war sat down to compare all the reliable maps of the moon which had been made down through

141

the ages. They were able to exhibit an impressive list of alterations which appeared to have taken place. Again, however, since these maps were made without benefit of photography, it was most difficult to determine if the changes were real, or if the observers were not accurate in recording what they saw.

Many of these ambiguities will soon be eliminated, because the Air Force has sponsored a moon-mapping project with the Lowell Observatory at Flagstaff, Arizona, which promises to produce a complete picture of the moon's near face with a great deal of new detail and with very high accuracy.

Several theories have been advanced to explain these variations on the moon's face. Perhaps our satellite is subject to the same quakes and eruptions which cause changes in the earth's topography. A Russian observer, Nikolai Kozyrev, noted what he termed a volcanic eruption on one of the central lunar mountains. Kozyrev was able to obtain spectrograms of this phenomenon which contained the element carbon. American astronomers are of the opinion that Kozyrev's find was not a true volcanic eruption but rather a simple release of gas, probably carbon dioxide.

The most common cause of lunar marks and scratches is undoubtedly meteorite strikes. The moon is an airless world without atmosphere to protect it from those fleet voyagers which, for the most part, burn up in the stratosphere before striking the surface of this globe. Meteor impacts must be very common on the moon and, indeed, the results of a few of them have already been seen from the earth.

Two astronomers involved in the moon-mapping program at Lowell Observatory saw three brief red spots on the moon's surface during the night of October 29, 1963. They were using Alvan Clark's famous 24-inch refractor at the time, and the spots were seen for about 20 minutes near the crater Aristarchus. A month later, on November 27, they saw another red spot on the same crater. This one lasted for more than an hour, so that they were able to alert other astronomers to observe the phenomenon. Observers at the Perkins Observatory, Delaware, Ohio, also saw this object, through a 69-inch reflector. Pictures taken with the 24-inch one, however, did not record the event.

Several astronomers have reported that small areas of the moon were temporarily obscured by lunar fog or haze; some have even observed that these faint clouds appear to drift across the moon's surface in a similar fashion to earth clouds. Most scientists are inclined to believe that there is an extremely rarefied layer of "atmosphere" on the moon which may be several miles deep. Certainly, the radioactive elements in the lunar crust must decay and thereby produce atmospheric gases. Most of these, such as hydrogen, are far too light to be held by the moon's weak gravitational field and are soon lost. The lunar atmosphere is probably made up of the heavier inert gases, such as argon, xenon, and krypton.

A few scientists have rationalized that some of the minor phenomena which have been observed on the moon could be explained by the existence of lunar plants, but they are the first to admit that such plant life must be very different from that of earth. There is no nourishing atmosphere, the temperature swings at least 200 degrees between day and night, and there is no water. While it is true that certain earth bacteria could survive under such conditions, they could exist only as dormant spores. In order for earth bacteria to reproduce and be active, they must have some of the comforts of life provided by the vast storehouse of earth. The environment of the moon is harsh and barren by comparison.

This means that *plant life as we know it* cannot thrive on the moon. From this, however, we cannot say that life on the moon is impossible. Not long after astronauts first set foot on the lunar surface, new spices and other rare delicacies may begin to grace our tables, just as they did in Europe after the voyages of Vasco da Gama and Columbus.

15 | THE PRINCESS OF OZ

In *The Wizard of Oz,* the Princess Ozma is the girl ruler of a land of mystery which is far, far away and is populated by exotic people who possess all manner of strange powers. The rewards for reaching the palace of the Wizard were great indeed—the lion is given courage, the tin man a heart, and the scarecrow a brain. Dorothy is put in a balloon and finds her way home. In this way each of the travelers achieves his fulfillment. Although the journey has been difficult and long, it has also been worthwhile.

No doubt Dr. Frank Drake of the National Radio Astronomy Observatory had some of these thoughts in mind when he was searching for a name for his project to attempt the detection of intelligent life on other planets. He called the experiment Project Ozma.

Earlier in this book we discussed the fact that it will probably be impossible for us ever to journey to the planets of other stars because of the vast distance which makes the flight too long and demands too much energy. Our brief lives are not designed for this sort of activity. We have also seen that it is not likely that we can hope to find other intelligent life equivalent to our own within the confines of our solar system.

But the possibilities exist for many planets such as ours which could have mothered and nurtured the development of life through the long ages required to bring forth that superb work of biological art—intelligent life. If scientists have performed their calculations properly, the heavens teem with opportunities. In our galaxy alone, there may be millions of such planets, and on many of them there is almost surely some form of *homo sapiens* or his equivalent.

It would be very bigoted of us to conclude that none of these creatures are ahead of us. Indeed, some of them must be like the great Wizard, possessed of truly magnificent powers which are certain to dazzle us so that we will stand before them like Dorothy and her friends—entranced with wonder.

The most practical way of contacting other intelligent creatures is by radio. The science of electronics is only slightly more than 50 years old, but it is one in which we are already nearing *technical perfection*. When scientists speak of reaching technical perfection, they mean that they have developed their knowledge and the-state-of-the-art to the point where the theoretical limits set by nature for their equipment have been reached. In an earlier chapter we noted that it was not practical to build larger astronomical telescopes on the surface of the earth because the atmosphere prevents us from seeing any more detail through them. Electronic science has progressed so rapidly that we are almost in the same position with radio. The sky background noise is now the most dominant factor in *hearing,* just as the atmospheric scatter has become the limiting element in *seeing.*

So far, the best of the available techniques have not been applied to the fascinating problem of contacting other intelligent life. The first attempt, however, was made by Dr. Frank Drake with his Project Ozma in April, May, June, and July of 1960.

Dr. Drake made a number of studies and comparisons before embarking on his search program. The most powerful radar in the United States at the time was one belonging to the Lincoln Laboratory of the Massachusetts Institute of Technology. Because of its location it is known as the Millstone Hill Radar. It demonstrated its true potential in 1959 when it bounced echoes off the planet Venus, and its effective radiating power has been calculated at better than 10 billion watts.

The National Radio Astronomy Observatory has an 85-foot antenna known as the Howard E. Tatel radio telescope, located in the Blue Ridge Mountains at Green Bank, West Virginia. Dr. Drake made some calculations using this instrument as a receiver and the powerful Millstone Hill Radar as a transmitter. He found that he could hear signals radiated by this great voice with his radio telescope even if they were transmitted from 8.7

light years away! There are a total of 11 stars within this distance, including three binary systems and the brightest star in the sky, Sirius.

From these calculations, Dr. Drake was able to formulate a rule of thumb for the distance at which good radio telescopes should be able to pick up the signals from reasonably powerful transmitters that might be used to contact other intelligent life.

He states: "The distance in light years at which strong present-day transmitters can be detected is about equal to the diameter of the receiving antenna in feet divided by 10."

The radio telescope located at Arecibo in Puerto Rico is 1,000 feet in diameter. The National Radio Astronomy Observatory also plans to build a 1,000-foot instrument. According to Dr. Drake's rule of thumb, these telescopes should be able to reach outward 100 light years to receive the signals of moderately high-power transmitters which we can build today after only 50 years' experience. There are more than 2,000 visible stars within this distance of the earth.

It appears that about 50 per cent of these systems are either binaries or more complex formations. Of the 100 nearest stars, 48 seem to be single stars, 40 are arranged as binaries, and 12 are in triple-star formations. Of the stars which are farther from the earth, more appear to be single stars, and there appear to be fewer multiple systems. However, this is most probably due to the limitations of our vision. It is increasingly difficult to discover the arrangement of star systems as their distance from us becomes greater.

Dr. Harrison Brown of the California Institute of Technology has recently completed a study of stellar systems which suggests a much higher frequency of planets than was formerly supposed. Dr. Brown points out that stars of less than 7 per cent of the mass of the sun do not emit visible light and therefore cannot be seen. We only know of their existence because, in many cases like that of the companion of Sirius, they affect the orbits of visible stars.

In order to understand Dr. Brown's theories, it is useful to be able to think in terms of *parsecs*. Astronomers calculate distances by measuring the amount of parallax, or change in angle, which a star exhibits when seen from the earth at opposite ends of its orbit. In other words, if an observer records the position of a star tonight and then again 6 months from now, he will have established its parallax angle. The parallax angle represents the apparent motion of a star due to the movement of the earth around the sun. Six months from now I will be halfway around the sun, or at maximum distance from my present position. This distance is about 186 million miles, and is called the base line. The distance from the sun to the earth is known as an astronomical unit.

About the beginning of the nineteenth century, when astronomers were just starting to measure the distances of some of the nearest stars, they found that a star which is 3.26 light years away would have a parallax angle of one second of arc when observed from the ends of the base line. They began to call this distance one parsec—a word coined from the two words, *par*allax and *sec*ond.

Astronomers have found that the 10,000 cubic parsecs of space around the sun contain about 1,000 visible stars. They have also noted that small and therefore dim stars are far more numerous than large hot ones. The reason we did not find this out a long time ago is that the smaller, dimmer stars are harder to see, unless they happen to be very close.

Because of the wobble they produce in the orbits of their accompanying bright suns, we know there are dark companions around seven nearby stars—eight if you include our own sun. Based on this data and the fact that the population increases as the size decreases, Dr. Brown has calculated that there must be over 12,000 invisible celestial bodies as large as the earth or larger, in the 10,000 cubic parsecs of space around the earth—a radius of less than 44 light years. He believes that there are over 60,000 bodies the size of Mars or larger in this same corner of space.

Dr. Brown also believes that about half of these bodies are organized in systems which do not have a central sun capable of transmitting enough heat to warm their surrounding planets. As pointed out in an earlier chapter, Dr. Harlow Shapley feels that some of these dark nomads may provide a suitable abode for life. A large percentage of the other 30,000 may be arranged in a way quite similar to that of our own solar system. Dr. Brown feels that the chances are good that most suns have a larger number of large planets, greater than asteroid size, than our sun. He feels the average might run as high as 50 planets per star.

As we have seen in earlier chapters, only a relatively few of the total planets have an atmosphere capable of supporting our type of carbon-based life. Not many have temperature extremes which lie within the boundaries which mark the lines of the freezing and the boiling points of water. It is therefore unlikely that any large portion of these planets nourish people like us— say, only one in every 25.

We are still left with a huge number: perhaps 200 billion in our galaxy, and more than 1,000 within 44 light years of the earth. Dr. Brown concludes his study by saying: "If planetary systems are indeed extremely abundant, one might conclude with equal conviction that man is not alone—that his equivalents may occupy hundreds or even thousands of bodies within our galaxy. With millions of planetary systems available in the galaxy, life forms may well be both abundant and diverse. Listening for evidence of the existence of such forms may indeed prove to be a profitable and exciting pursuit."

Although all of these ideas had not been advanced when Frank Drake began his Project Ozma to search for intelligent life in space, the possibilities of such a program had already generated a great deal of excitement in the minds of many scientists.

During the last few years astronomers have suggested that there is a growing body of evidence that planets are the rule rather than the exception in space. Making calculations similar to those of Dr. Brown, and allowing for the development of life on one planet in 25, it can be shown that there should be more than 15,000 such planets within reach of the National Radio Astronomy Observatory's proposed 1,000-foot dish. Indeed,

Frank Drake and others were saying that there might possibly be a few within range of the present 85-foot radio telescope.

There is still another aspect of this problem which has stimulated the interest of many scientists. We have nearly achieved technical perfection in electronics during the very brief period of about 50 years. Measured against the vast time constants of the universe, 50 years is less than a cosmic instant—about 100 millionth of the age of the earth. On the cosmic time scale, therefore, a civilization passes in a most abrupt fashion from a position of having no radio capability to technical perfection. Once such a capability is in hand, it is probably not lost, provided the possessing society is sufficiently mature to avoid destroying itself by the use of atomic bombs, or by other equally deadly devices which we have fortunately not discovered yet.

Here, then, was a situation which would excite the imagination of any thinking man. Humans are in the midst of this rapid transition between a non-communicating society and one which has a full radio capability. We are surrounded in space by stars other than our sun, some of which probably support planets having civilizations in a far more advanced stage of development than our own. Should we not cock our ears to see if we can find any understandable star talk?

Most scientists felt that the answer to this question had to be "yes," and Dr. Drake had no trouble in gaining the necessary support for his program. Quickly he set about formulating a plan of attack.

First of all, he must decide on which frequency to conduct his search. At the extremely low frequencies the background noise would smother signals from even our nearest neighbors. At the very high frequencies, the atmospheric blanket blocks them out. As we have noted in an earlier chapter, the great signpost among frequencies in the cosmos is 1,420.4 megacycles, the radiation frequency of atomic hydrogen.

Of course one would not want to listen exactly on 1,420.4 megacycles, because the background noise of hydrogen itself would overwhelm the signals of any lesser transmitter. It would be most desirable to explore either side of this sign post, covering an area of a few hundred kilocycles each way. Dr. Drake decided to explore a total frequency band of 400 kilocycles around the hydrogen emission frequency.

The next question was where to search.

Obviously, Dr. Drake had to pick a nearby star. His equipment was not designed to search for star talk, and was not strong enough to reach those which are far distant. The time for that would come later when larger, more efficient instruments were available.

The nearest star of all is Alpha Centauri, only 4.3 light years away. Unfortunately, Alpha Centauri is not a single star, but consists of one large body with similar radiation characteristics as our sun, and two smaller companions which are hot enough to emit light, and are therefore stars and not planets. Planets that were caught in the gravity field of such a system would have very complex orbits varying extensively from one revolution to the next. The amount of light and heat they would receive from their parent stars would also fluctuate drastically—much too widely for them to maintain the narrow limits necessary for the nourishment of life.

Moving outward, the next object we come to is Barnard's star, which is known to possess at least one planet whose mass is not more than 50 per cent greater than that of Jupiter. But the light from Barnard's star grows dim. Although it is only 6 light years away, it is too faint to be seen without the aid of a reasonably powerful telescope. The life zone which must be occupied by its planets if civilizations are to exist is far too narrow. Regretfully, we must decide it is not a fertile spot and move on.

The next star, named for its discoverer, is known as Wolf 359. It is 7.74 light years away, and again far too dim, having a visual magnitude of 13.5. Luyten 726 A and B are only 7.9 light years away, but they form a very faint binary system—not a good abode for life. Lalande 21185 is 8.2 light years distant but is also a binary, and faint. The next objects are Sirius A and B. Sirius A is the brightest object in the sky, certainly hot enough to support any number of life-bearing planets. Sirius B is a dwarf companion, and the two stars form a system which is 8.7 light years away. Because of the mutual attraction of their gravity fields, the two stars wobble considerably on their journey through space. Indeed, it was through this wobble effect that scientists initially discovered the existence of Sirius B, and it was the first such companion star ever found. Sirius A is a relatively new star, both young and hot. It has probably not been a main sequence star long enough to foster the development of intelligent life. For this reason, and also because of the strong gravitational pull of its companion, we must reluctantly move along to more distant stars. The next two stars, Ross 154 and Ross 348, are far too dim and small to support life.

After them we come to Epsilon Eridani, a most interesting star from the standpoint of our search. Like our own sun, it has been a main sequence star long enough to nurture life. It is not as bright as our sun, but still bright enough, and the analysis of its spectrum tells us that it is rotating slowly, just like two-thirds of the other stars in our galaxy. This probably means that it has lost some of its angular momentum to planets and may well have a number of them in orbit around it. Epsilon Eridani is 10.8 light years from the sun.

We must pass over a total of 11 more stars before we reach another likely candidate. This one is Tau Ceti, at 11.8 light years. It is larger and brighter than Epsilon Eridani, although still smaller than the sun. In all respects it is an excellent possibility.

Within the first 12 light years from our solar system we have been able to find two stars which fulfill the basic requirements for supporting life. Both are somewhat beyond the modest range of Frank Drake's 85-foot radio telescope, but perhaps the citizens of these far-off worlds are not power-limited to the same extent as we are, and we may still hear them if we listen closely enough.

In order to find these two stars, we searched through the nearest 26 celestial objects outside the solar system. By proceeding outward to 16 light years, we would have had 46 stars to search through. Each additional light year thereafter will bring forth an increasingly larger harvest. As a result, on a statistical basis, the chances of

151

detecting intelligent life will increase drastically with increased radio-telescope range.

Dr. Drake made a number of other calculations before undertaking Project Ozma. Because his radio ear was so weak, he knew that his chances were not very good, and that a very powerful radio indeed must be beamed his way if he was to hear anything at all. In fact, he calculated that a 1,000,000-watt transmitter must be transmitting via a 600-foot antenna if he were to receive its signals.

Nevertheless it was worth a try. Beginning in the spring of 1960, Dr. Drake undertook his historic search. About 3 o'clock in the morning of April 6, 1960, he pointed the huge ear toward Tau Ceti and turned on the receiver. Man's first experiment in attempting to make contact with life beyond his own planet was under way. As the big telescope followed the star across the sky, the tape recorders silently wrote the journal of all that was heard. Finally, as Tau Ceti slowly slid below the West Virginia hills, Dr. Drake swung his instrument around until it picked up Epsilon Eridani.

Various frequencies were searched on both planets. All signals picked up were carefully recorded so that they could be rigorously analyzed later to determine if they contained the slightest coherency—this being the astronomer's way of describing signals which contain intelligent communications instead of mere random noise.

The very first night that the telescope was directed toward Epsilon Eridani it picked up a coherent signal! Needless to say, the astronomers were excited. They felt that they were perhaps taking part in one of the all-time great moments of science. Dr. Drake was later asked what his initial thoughts were on receiving this first signal from outer space. He replied: "I wondered if perhaps the equipment had failed."

Unfortunately, when the antenna was moved, the signal persisted, showing that it was merely a powerful emission from some earth-borne transmitter, and not from the vicinity of Epsilon Eridani. No other intelligent signals were received, and after about 150 hours of searching the telescope had to be taken off Project Ozma for other important research programs.

Dr. Drake has pointed out that we should not be discouraged at the failure of this first humble effort. Only two of the hundreds of possible star targets had been examined. The telescope was far from an ideal instrument for the job, and many years of effort in a planned program with large instruments and highly sensitive receivers would be required for a good chance of success.

Other telescopes in addition to those previously mentioned are being built which will be much better adapted for this sort of work. Among these is the 140-foot antenna which is now being built for the National Radio Astronomy Observatory. In a few years there will be many more.

Recently there has been some evidence that Russian scientists have also undertaken a project to listen for intelligent signals from other planets. In March, 1964, Moscow reported that two Soviet astronomers had detected what were believed to be signals from "highly developed beings," originating on a planet revolving around one of the two stars which form 61 Cygni, about 11.1 light years away, closer than Tau Ceti but further away than Epsilon Eridani.

It has been known for some time that one of these double stars has an unseen companion about 17 times heavier than Jupiter. This body is assumed to be a planet, since it is too small to support the nuclear reaction necessary to generate the heat of even a miniature sun. Its existence was established in the same manner as that of the dark star around Sirius, namely, by its effect on the orbits of the parent stars. However, scientists still have not been able to determine if it orbits about 61 Cygni A or B.

In any event, U.S. scientists have been somewhat skeptical of this report for several reasons. Although the 61 Cygni stars are main sequence suns, they are relatively small and dim. Their combined visual luminosity is less than one-tenth that of our sun, therefore the life zones of their planets would be extremely narrow. The life zones are further limited by the fact that the stars form a binary

In addition, this report contained some highly controversial speculations about the connection between these signals and several earth catastrophies, such as the volcanic eruption of Krakatoa in 1883 which completely obliterated this island, and the great meteor of 1908 in northern Siberia which caused immense devastation. The inference of the report was that these two events were somehow controlled by the "highly developed beings."

In May, 1966, it was revealed by the International Astronomical Union that a proposal for a multi-nation effort to search for signals from the worlds had been submitted by the Soviet Academy of Sciences. The plan for the project was outlined in a paper by Professor V. C. Troitsky of the Academy of Sciences who was listed as "president of the section for the detection of signals from extraterrestrial civilizations."

The Soviet proposal envisioned a search for two kinds of signals. The first program would be for the purpose of seeking out the narrow-band signals beamed forth by civilizations like ours who have relatively limited energy available for such a project. The paper points out that to explore all stars within 1,000 light years at all frequencies would require many observatories working for hundreds of years. It suggests that an attempt be made to isolate the most likely candidates and limit the frequencies by searching in the vicinity of "the great landmark" at 21 centimeters, just as proposed by Frank Drake during Project Ozma.

Numerous Soviet scientists have expressed the belief that intelligent life is not only restricted to the earth. Some of them feel that the nearest civilization comparable to ours may be found within 1,000 light years. Dr. Dmitry Martinov, head of the Sternberg Institute, has speculated in the Soviet popular science magazine, *Tekhnika Molodezpi,* that an advanced civilization is very likely to make its existence known to others because of emotions such as altruism, curiosity and vanity.

The second Soviet proposed quest would be for signals of broad spectrum and much greater energy. Professor Troitsky draws attention to the newly discovered quasars which radiate incredible amounts of energy over a wide frequency range. He states that these great energy

154

sources might be the beacons of super civilizations who have advanced far beyond us along the evolutionary ladder. Because of the sophistication of these broadcasters, Soviet scientists feel that we may have a difficult time distinguishing artificial messages from such an advanced civilization from the natural radio noise generated in the universe. We could expect, once we have succeeded in decoding them, that these signals would be crammed with advanced knowledge.

The Soviet programs call for an international program of around-the-clock observations lasting for several years. Already this idea has generated a great deal of interest in scientists throughout the world.

The future rests on the availability of better radio telescopes. We will soon be able to build larger and more efficient instruments outside the earth's gravitational field on the surface of the moon or on stations which have been placed in earth orbits. In addition to eliminating the problem of the earth's gravity, these stations will not be subjected to the attenuation of the earth's atmosphere which blankets many of the frequencies that are most interesting. The moon exerts a pull of gravity about one-sixth that of the earth. This will still permit the building of much larger telescopes for both visual and radio astronomy. All scientists are eagerly looking forward to the day when these programs will unveil many more wonders of the universe.

16 | THE CELESTIAL CENTAURS

Of all earth's creatures, we alone speak and think and feel in the unique way which has enabled us to progress at an ever-accelerating pace. As a result, many historians feel that human knowledge was doubled for the first time by 1700, doubled again by 1900, again by 1950, and yet again by 1960. Because our learning curve sweeps always upward, we have far outstripped our earthly competitors to the point where we alone of all the many man-apes who roamed the earth during the Pliocene period are still around. We have competed all the others into extinction.

How much of this development is the result of chance? How much is the inevitable conclusion of a fixed design made rigid by the harsh requirements of a hostile environment? Can we use ourselves as a mirror to show the characteristics of life on other planets?

Certainly any creatures we can converse with over the vast distances of interstellar space must be able to talk among themselves. In addition to organs of speech, they must also have working hands, and brains to think with. One of the major lessons of our own biology is that creatures who have no arms and hands are no real competitors in the race for evolutionary achievement, however intelligent they may be.

A growing number of anthropologists believe that we are wandering about on two legs primarily because we started out with a total of only four limbs, and it was necessary for us to learn to walk upright if we were to have arms and hands. Many have asked themselves the question: Wouldn't we be better off with more appendages?

The choice for extra limbs existed at the time the early fish invaded the land. The amphibians that crawled up from the sea kept only four major appendages out of the original stock; the rest of us have been limited ever since.

If our ancestors had not been so feckless, or had been possessed of more foresight, men today might be walking about on the sturdy underpinning of four legs instead of two, like the mythical centaurs described in the ancient legends.

But would we really be better off?

In most ways the answer is probably yes. Indeed, Dr. William Howells, professor of anthropology at Harvard University, has said: "I will lay a small bet that the first men we contact from outer space will be neither bipeds nor quadrupeds, but bimanous quadrupedal hexapods." In other words, he believes they will have six limbs—two hands and four feet.

He goes on to say that man is probably as large as it is safe for him to be with his present configuration. "The men of elsewhere are probably not giants either if they must stand on only two legs. But if they have four feet to hold them, then they might be as big as a horse, or even larger, and still be both intelligent and maneuverable."

As related in an earlier chapter, many factors influence the development of the species, and each must be tailored to its specific environment. Creatures who live on small worlds of low gravity will not have the heavy body structures of those who must exist under the yoke of a heavy gravitational load. Atmospheres different from our own would surely produce quite different body types. Rather minor changes in environmental stresses might cause major changes in planetary biology.

Dr. Howells has also speculated about what would occur if human life was suddenly wiped from the earth. He asks the question: "Would intelligent life rise again? If so, how long would it take?"

He is quite doubtful about the immediate prospects. All of man's really close relations are gone. Apes might move up, but monkeys have not become more like humans in the past 35 million years.

No other creatures are available to begin a new race of intelligent animals, according to Dr. Howells. He points out that cats, snakes, birds, and dogs are far too deeply involved in their present ways to become men if we are swept away. The next try would have to come from something like the small tree shrew, Tupaia, from far down the evolutionary pecking order. Tupaia must slowly and painfully repeat all of early primate history. At best, it would take a long, long time.

Time alone, however, would not be enough. Perhaps even more important to the regeneration of intelligent life on this globe would be the elimination of the predatory beasts which would almost certainly destroy the ambitious primates before they completed the long journey to human intelligence. As Dr. Howells says: "Before little Tupaia could put forth progressive descendants now, the world would have to be swept clean of the kind of competition which might overcome them on the way up. This means get rid of most higher animals, above all, rats, cats, and monkeys."

If for any reason Tupaia failed, there would be slight chance for other intelligent life beginning partway up the evolutionary tree. The remaining links between the beginning and the end product have long since vanished.

In this case we would need brand-new vertebrates. In order to get them, we must begin all over again. "Eradicate the fish," Dr. Howells says. "For they rule the seas as we rule the land, and they are not likely to stand aside while nature experiments with ridiculously crude forerunners of fish-like animals once more. Conceivably, to become intelligent, life would have to start afresh. In that case wipe out everything that moves to keep the necessary simple molecules from being eaten as they form.

"All in all," concludes Professor Howells, "our hopes for repetition are not good. We had better stay the hand that drops the bomb."

Although the hopes of repetition are not good, the possibility that intelligence will ultimately arise, once life gains a foothold, is excellent. And when intelligence does take hold and begins to develop, the results are truly spectacular.

The clues existing in the caves and burial grounds suggest that our early pre-history began with the origin of men-like creatures who were able to develop a crude and rudimentary technology based on the use of sticks and stones. This pre-history began perhaps a million years ago, and lasted until about 6000 B.C. During this period at least four major types of man-like beasts emerged: *Australopithecus, Pithecanthropus, Neanderthal,* and *Homo Sapiens,* the latter of which managed to prevail.

Our later pre-history began about 6000 B.C. and lasted until 1000 B.C. By this time only one man-like creature still survived, and we are all his descendants. He was not only able to walk but he had also invented the ship and subjugated the riding animals, both of which provided him with more efficient ways of getting about. One might say that we who have survived have consolidated

158

all our main gains since that time—a matter of no more than 3000 years. This vertical explosion of knowledge and capability is by far the most spectacular achievement of life on our planet. The transition from complete ignorance to intellectual sophistication has been achieved at an unbelievable pace, and it is this rapid development which provides us with one of the best arguments for a program to search for intelligent life on other planets.

Scientists have succeeded in writing a formula to express the probability of communicating with life on other worlds. Quite often this formula is written as follows: $N = N_s f_p n_e f_b n_i f_c L_c / L_p$.

In this formula N is equal to the number of planets in our galaxy where we can expect to find intelligent life which is attempting to communicate with us. N_s represents the number of suitable stars which have been on main sequence long enough to allow the evolution of an intelligent species. The biological development of life on the earth has taken 4.5 billion years; and since we have nothing better to go on, we might use this as an average figure. We must therefore exclude the very young stars as well as the very old. In addition, we should eliminate those which are so faint as to have extremely narrow life zones, as well as most of those which are arranged as binaries or other multiple-star groups. If we rule out all these, leaving only those which are quite like our sun, we still have a number of stars equal to about 10 followed by 10 zeros.

The function of f_p represents the fraction of stars which have planetary systems. Many scientists feel that all single stars of main sequence have planets; however, in order to be conservative, let us assume that only 50 per cent possess them.

The next symbol in our formula, n_o, requires that we attempt to answer the questions: What percentage of all planets can be expected to support life? This will depend primarily on the answers to two other questions. First, how many planets lie within the life zone of each star? And second, how large are they? As we have seen earlier, both Earth and Mars lie within the life zone of our sun. Venus may also be in the running, but as yet we cannot be sure. Life-supporting planets must be large enough to capture and hold an atmosphere of the heavier gases; and while there is no definite upper limit to their size, the force of gravity becomes a serious problem on the large, dense planets. Moreover, the atmosphere of large planets is likely to contain a significant amount of hydrogen, which has a strong disadvantage from the standpoint of carbon-based life. Based on earth experience, n_e might be equal to a figure of about 20 per cent.

f_b represents the percentage of planets which will produce life if the conditions are favorable. Most biologists feel that 100 per cent of the planets which have the right conditions for life will support life if there is time for it to develop. Therefore f_b is equal to one. If we can demonstrate that life, even though it be very rudimentary, exists on Mars, we will have gone a long way toward proving the validity of this figure.

Perhaps n_i is the most interesting and controversial of all the factors. This represents the number of planets per solar system likely to develop creatures with the ability to communicate with their neighbors in space. In the case of our own sun, we can begin to suspect that n_i is at least equal to one. In an earlier chapter we discussed the fact that other creatures, particularly dolphins, possess a high order of intelligence. However, in order to communicate with other life, it is not sufficient just to be intelligent; one must also have developed technical capability as well. It appears that no other inhabitants of our solar system have developed a technical society. Perhaps we would not go very far astray if we let n_i equal one.

The next symbol, f_c, represents that fraction of the technological societies which wishes to communicate with others. We can assume that the possibilities are quite high that most technical and intelligent societies will ultimately become interested in interstellar communications once they are convinced that there are others worth communicating with. According to our own experience, this realization begins to dawn at about the time that technical capability for communications appears. The desire to listen and to be heard is surely universal. Probably it is reasonable to estimate f_c as 100 per cent.

L_c is an estimate of the lifetime of a planet, once

160

its citizens have achieved the ability and the desire to engage in interstellar communications. This figure, of course, remains a great uncertainty, because societies appear to develop the capability to commit suicide by the time they have learned the basic facts necessary for long-distance communications. Recently, some scientists have been willing to speculate that we might recover our technical capability rather quickly after a nuclear war, provided it was not totally devastating. Even so, the possibilities of the thermo-nuclear termination to our technology are quite large and cannot be discounted. We have been in the nuclear age for only a quarter of a century, and human ingenuity will surely create more destructive devices that will ultimately become so cheap that even small, unstable nations can possess them.

In addition, cultures on the earth have demonstrated a tendency to wax and wane. Chinese culture, which exhibited more ability to survive than any other, lasted about 1,000 years—less than an instant on the cosmic timetable. However, we appear to be entering a new era wherein cultures are not limited by geography, but are world-wide. As we learn to communicate with other worlds, they may teach us a few things about the ability to survive that will help us to last longer.

There are a number of other effects which may influence the time period during which society may engage in interstellar communications. Perhaps after a while a society will lose interest and sign off the celestial network. For want of a better figure, let us assume that the average society will remain on the communications network for about 1,000,000 years, once it starts communicating. Hence, L_c is equal to 1,000,000.

The quantity L_p is the estimated lifetime of a planet after the emergence of intelligent life. This value must be very large, since the lifetime of our galaxy is about 10 followed by 10 zeros years old, and most of the stars were formed in the first few billion years. L_p is probably at least equal to 10 followed by 9 zeros.

On the basis of these estimates, the number of advanced civilizations that may attempt to communicate with us in our own galaxy is quite large indeed, being equal to at least 1,000,000. After completing somewhat similar calculations, Dr. Sebastian von Hoerner of the Astronomisches Rechen-Institut, Heidelberg, Germany, has suggested that we might expect to find the ten nearest technical civilizations within 1,000 light years of the sun. Dr. A. G. W. Cameron of NASA believes that the closest advanced civilization should be within 300 light years.

Since 300 light years is a long transmission time, even for a celestial telegram, we might expect that our fraternizing neighbors will not wait for replies. Right away they will surely send some information about themselves, and perhaps some ideas based on their most sophisticated knowledge. They will probably speak to us first in pictures. There will be no great hurry, and the pictures will be filled with many details. They may also set up a listening schedule for our part of the galaxy, and they will surely let us know their program so that we can talk back to them. Because of the long time scale involved, the mutual exchange of ideas will be a slow process.

Advanced civilizations which happen to develop on the planets of the same sun or nearby suns are at a considerable advantage. The ability to establish early and effective communications with adjacent sophisticated societies is indeed a most fortunate happenstance.

We are solely the product of this world, the earth. Our point of view and our development are restricted to the confines of this insignificant corner of the cosmos. There can be no doubt that we could receive incalculable benefits if we could profit from the experience and knowledge of people who have developed in other corners, with other points of view. The proximity of an intelligent, technical, and advanced civilization which could not destroy us because of the great barrier of space would be truly a lucky break.

The brief records and the scanty amount of information in books that contain our total knowledge have been collected only lately and at great labor. All that we know of the universe is the product of our own harsh and restricted environment. The ability to sharpen our knowledge by the exchange of knowledge with a truly foreign society will be the source of untold riches.

There are certain to be many surprises contained in

the interstellar messages. We are sure to begin by sitting at the feet of those who are much older—in terms of civilization—and wiser than we, since the ability to transmit requires far greater development than the ability to listen.

What will they tell us?

They will be very advanced in radio astronomy, and more steeped in the cosmic culture than our own scientists are. As a result, they can tell us much about the universe which would take us centuries to learn if we were left on our own. Along with many practical things, they will answer some of the basic questions that have intrigued man since he first began to wonder about his relationship to the vast celestial order.

However, we may find that we also are able to contribute to the general knowledge of the cosmic network. It is possible that there may be gaps that we alone can fill; after a short period of listening we may find many reasons for going on the air ourselves to add our own small voice to the others.

We can expect that the great radio stations in space will transmit messages which can be divided into two types, just like those of the amateur radio operators who converse with each other every night. They will first transmit probing messages, or call signs, which will ask others to talk with them. These messages will also contain vast amounts of information and be very cleverly designed, if for no other reason than to induce others to communicate with them.

The second class of messages will be for the purpose of transmitting information. These may be sent only to those who have already sent answers back. On the other hand, they may be beamed toward people such as we who are on the verge of developing a cosmic communications capability. It may be that highly advanced civilizations have developed ways of sorting out stars in such a fashion that they can forecast the likely candidates. Already we are beginning to explore a few of the possibilities for doing this. By being able to estimate the luminosity of a star, its age, and whether or not it is accompanied by companion stars which will restrict the planetary life zones, it is possible to reduce by a considerable amount the total number of suns which should be investigated. On the basis of these considerations, we can already say that of the fifty stars nearest the earth, the sun is by far the most likely to have life-supporting planets. Our sun is the right age, it is a single star, and it is sufficiently bright to have a reasonably wide life zone.

Societies which have developed the technology and the sophistication necessary to communicate with their neighbors also understand the universe better than we do. They will possess instruments and techniques that enable them to search for intelligent life-sustaining planets much more efficiently than we can in our present stage of development.

Perhaps the strongest indication of this is that although we are merely on the threshold of investigating other life-bearing planets, we have already learned a great deal about the problems. Already we have found planets around some of the adjacent stars. For example, we have discovered the planet which revolves around Barnard's star, and this object has a mass only 50 per cent greater than that of Jupiter.

Once the facility for sending cosmic messages is established, the cost of transmitting them becomes insignificant. The major disadvantage of sending messages to the vicinity of stars which do not respond arises from the fact that it may result in wasting time for no useful purpose. It is an unprofitable enterprise, like knocking on the door long after it is obvious that no one is home.

The nearest and most likely candidates will surely receive the most attention. Who can be sure that some distant scientist is not knocking at the door of this planet right now—waiting in the celestial darkness for someone to answer?

As we have slowly climbed the Great Tower of Discovery, our conception of the human position in the vast celestial universe has slowly but persistently diminished. Copernicus shifted the center from the earth to the sun. The work of Newton, Huygens, and others soon proved that even this regal body was not the focus. Thus we were moved even further from the center of things.

Through much groping we have achieved a more humble if more realistic view of our true place in the cosmic order. In size, we are about halfway between the atom and the sun. In age, we are incredibly young when measured by celestial clocks. In both capability and understanding we are poor citizens, at present limited to the most simple problems. In composition, we are of the same unexceptional chemicals as all other living things. In terms of power to command the great forces around us, we are quite insignificant.

But all is not lost. Even though we are without consequence in size, time, and power, we still may not be totally unimportant. In our corner of the cosmos, man alone forgives. Compassion and pity appear to be luxuries available only to the most favored in a universe totally devoted to the survival of the fittest. In ability to contemplate and progress, we are quite remarkable, as far as we can see. We have an appreciation of beauty and a great hungry curiosity. All such values may be more significant than we now think.

Perhaps we will achieve a better appreciation for the relative importance of these things once we begin to add our voices to those of the remote citizenry of other planets. Along with learning of the biology, chemistry, and physics of other societies, we will want to know of their art and their philosophy.

Dr. Philip Morrison of Cornell University said in a recent lecture before the Philosophical Society of Washington: "What is still interesting is clearly the experience of our fellows. . . . What are their novels? What are the art histories? What are the anthropological problems of these distant stars? That is the kind of material these remote philosophers have been chewing over for a long time. Do they want to know about the earth?"

If we can measure our own thought, art, and even perhaps our social mores against those of other societies representing very different environments and points of view, it will surely enrich the understanding and appreciation of our basic human position.

Like the new boy in school, we will soon be tested and quickly find our place. In the process of meeting these other civilizations, we will surely learn more about ourselves and perhaps will learn about what has been termed the "posthuman" activity which faces our successors in the future.

It has been suggested by Dr. Morrison and others that the main groups from distant populations who will be interested in us are the anthropologists and those sociologists whose interests lie in primitive life. They will probably have outdone us technically and scientifically, and will be far ahead of us in sophistication and culture, so that some of our conversation may be a bit boring to them.

They may be primarily interested in conversing with us for the same reason that we are exploring Mars and the moon. It will add to their general knowledge of life in the universe and perhaps fill in a few missing links in their past. As Morrison has said: "Their Department of Anthropology will maintain primitive signaling devices meant to catch those people who cannot do very much better. The anthropologists will feel that it would be nice to see how the primitives could enter their interesting society."

How will they seek to contact us?

Dr. Morrison feels that we need not look for really complicated methods. He says: "If we wished to land on the Queensland coast and talk to the aborigines, we

166

would hardly set up a TV station and broadcast a program. We would rather use some simple audible means, like a steam whistle and a drum. Then these people who are sure to have that sort of communication will come to see what it is we have to sell, give away, or trade, or what news we have to spread. So it is with civilizations and the universe."

A number of scientists have advanced the view that highly civilized cultures may have developed ways of detecting societies which are about to enter the stellar communications network. Several ways of doing this have been suggested. One such scheme involves placing satellites in orbit around those stars that show promise of decreased angular momentum and adequate life zones which have been on the main sequence long enough to allow life to become well advanced. Our sun must surely stand out like a beacon as a prime example—after all, we are here!

Such a satellite need not be large, perhaps a carefully designed one the size of a watermelon would do. It need not listen or transmit continuously either. When the planets of a star begin to "awaken," the satellite could flash the news home so that an intensive program of interstellar communication could be placed in operation. It has also been suggested that such a satellite might broadcast earth signals, and thus indicate the stage of our development.

There have already been reports of signals retransmitted or echoed after a time delay. In 1927 and again in 1934, a Norwegian scientist, Carl Stormer, reported hearing radio signals originating in Holland retransmitted about 15 seconds after their original transmission. There have been a number of attempts to explain such phenomena as echoes produced by the ionized solar clouds, but none have been entirely satisfactory.

One could postulate that a really advanced civilization might scatter quite a number of such satellites or intelligence-seeking probes through the universe. Relay stations to pass the weak signals generated by such robots on to their masters at home could be placed around some of the brighter stars, whose energy can be used in some form of solar battery to generate the power needed to operate them. In a few years we may be capable of undertaking this sort of activity ourselves.

Actually, these robots could perform far more useful tasks—if they were designed by generous as well as very advanced scientists. They could contain tapes recording knowledge which had been carefully selected as being the most beneficial for blossoming societies. Perhaps they might contain useful information such as how to convert from predatory local policies to truly peaceful ones, once hydrogen bombs have been manufactured. Such satellites might advise us with ideas on how to speed our technological growth even faster. In fact, there are no limits to the good uses such a satellite could be put to if built for helpful purposes by an advanced civilization. It is possible that such a cosmic encyclopedia even now awaits without, prevented from pouring out its storehouse of knowledge only by our inability to produce the key to unlock its voice.

There are other ways perhaps even more practical that are available to a truly enlightened technology for detecting intelligent life on distant worlds. In a few years we will be placing astronomical observations in orbiting satellites and on the moon. They will be less hampered by gravity and by atmospheric attenuation. Who knows what the limiting sizes of such space-borne antennas will be? Already scientists are saying that electronic ears as large as 10,000 feet in diameter may be possible. According to Frank Drake's rule of thumb, such antennas should be able to detect interstellar communications signals at distances up to 1,000 light years. They could also eavesdrop on the *routine daily electronic traffic* of a planet like the earth out to perhaps 50 light years!

Ironically, the first indications which cultured citizens from outside the solar system may have of our existence may be the vapid and tasteless commercial products of our television and radio industry. After such an introduction, if they are still willing to contact us we will be fortunate indeed.

Frank Drake and others have mentioned the use of correlation techniques which allow signals to be piled on top of each other by means of time-delay circuits. This results in a considerable reinforcement of the original weak level. Improved parametric amplifiers and other new techniques will also assist us to reach out farther with electronic listening devices. Drake has said: "These approaches suggest that our civilization may itself be easily detected, despite our failure to send out signals for that specific purpose."

In addition to the electromagnetic spectrum, it may be possible to communicate with other civilizations using the oldest and perhaps most reliable of all systems—known among technicians as the Mark One Eyeball, in other words the simple old-fashioned faculty of sight. The techniques involved are new and extremely exciting. The principles were developed mainly during the last decade by Dr. Charles Townes of MIT, who recently won the Nobel Prize and is known as the father of the *maser* and *laser*.

Of these two devices, the maser was invented first, in 1954. The word is coined from the scientific phrase "microwave amplification by stimulated emission of radiation"—which does not help most people in defining the new, somewhat complex principles of physics which permit the device to work. The maser is a way of using high-energy or "excited" molecules to interact with other molecules to produce still more exitation. Such excited molecules give off waves on the electromagnetic frequencies, and are able to reinforce or amplify each other when they are placed in the electronic equivalent of an echo chamber. Thus the maser becomes an extremely effective and powerful amplifier.

Four years later, Dr. Townes was able to accomplish the same sort of amplification for light, using ruby crystals on a resonant chamber built of mirrors. On May 9, 1962, scientists at MIT used one of their lasers to produce a 6-inch beam of light which they directed at the new moon. The dark surface was sufficiently illuminated so that the change in brightness could be detected by the MIT engineers.

Dr. Townes believes that other technological civilizations may have refined these new techniques much more than we have. Indeed, they may have reversed our history and stumbled on the optical amplification methods earlier than the electronic systems. Even with the present elementary state of earth-borne lasers, calculations have shown that a laser coupled with the 200-inch Mount Palomar telescope would produce a signal bright enough to be seen 10 light years away—through another Mount Palomar telescope. With the naked eye, it could still be seen over distances of about one tenth of a light year.

There are difficulties, however, with the transmission of signals by flashing lights. We have known how to build optical telescopes for over 300 years, yet the largest in operation is no more than 200 inches in diameter. The great electronic dish at Arecibo, Puerto Rico, is 1,000 feet across, and we have been building electronic mirrors for only two decades.

This is largely due to the stringent accuracy requirements for optical instruments because of the short wave length of light. The surface of an optical mirror must be true within millionths of an inch, while the face of a radio dish may be out by an eighth of an inch or more. As Frank Drake has said: "These accuracy limitations are not peculiar to ourselves, but are common to all civilizations everywhere." Probably, because of the implacable nature of these physical laws, we can be fairly certain that others as well as ourselves have found they can do a better job with radio.

Some scientists, notably Philip Morrison, have even dared to ponder the possibility of communicating with the intelligent life of other galaxies, although most confine their thoughts to local stars. In no small measure this is because Andromeda, our nearest neighboring collection of suns, is 2.2 million light years away, no mean distance even for armchair theorists.

Morrison feels that within this magnificent faraway island of more than 100 billion suns there must surely be extremely advanced civilizations. He realizes that it would be most difficult for us to communicate with them because of the vast power requirements and the long transmission time, but he has still suggested a possibility: "I can think of only one or two ways to signal them, which sound far beyond the capacity of men. Maybe one of the stars can be modulated by interposing an opaque screen. It would have to weigh about 22 followed by 17 zeros pounds (the mass of a comet), distributed in micron-size particles over a 5-degree zone of a sphere surrounding the star, and moving in an orbit like the orbit of a planet."

There might be ways, according to Morrison, of changing the orbit or shape of this screen in such a way that it would modulate the light of a star in a manner that could be used to transmit intelligent messages to other galaxies. Morrison concludes: "Perhaps in that remote galaxy, some patient signalers have for 50 million years tried to modulate a star . . . These ideas are real ones, and not meant to be taken wholly lightly. I think I am not producing science fiction, but legitimate speculation of demonstrable plausibility."

Even more exotic ideas have come from other scientists who have considered the problem. One such is Dr. Freeman Dyson, who is presently at the Institute for Advanced Study, Princeton University, who has thought about the sort of intelligent citizens we might expect to find in space.

Dyson points out that the time required for the development of industrial and technical capabilities is extremely short compared with the time scale of stellar evolution. He feels, therefore, that we may find civilizations which are several millions of years old and very much further ahead than we are, at least in a technical and scientific sense. In fact, he says that some may have already reached the limits set by Malthusian principles.

He then draws attention to the work of Thomas R. Malthus, an English political economist of the early nineteenth century. Malthus produced the theory that population increases as a geometric progression, while the means to support life moves upward as an arithmetic progression. The ultimate result of such a development is that a society ultimately reaches a point where it bumps against an upper limit based on the supply of energy and material available for its exploitation.

Dyson postulates that in our own case we will be approaching the Malthusian limit when we have taken advantage of the total radiation of the sun and the total mass of all its surrounding planets. He points out that although this idea appears foolish at first, with some re-arrangement of our solar system it becomes reasonably practical.

For example, if all the materials in the planets were to be distributed in the form of a spherical shell revolving around the sun, such a shell would be about 10 feet thick if it were located a distance of twice the earth's orbit. Of course such a sphere could not be solid, but must be formed of a collection of small objects in separate orbits around the sun. It could, however, be made quite habitable with all the comforts necessary to support a maximum of advanced citizens in a manner and style befitting their technical competence. Along with utilizing all the available solar system real estate, it would also make use of the sun's radiant energy falling on it from the inside.

Once a society has begun to "go technical," observes Dyson, its progress is almost like that of an atomic chain reaction. He feels that we of earth may find our heads knocking against the Malthusian limits in a relatively few thousand years. Dyson states: "It seems, then, a reasonable expectation that, barring accidents, Malthusian pressures will ultimately drive an intelligent species to adopt some such efficient exploitation of its available resources. One should expect that, within a few thousand years of its entering the stage of industrial development, any intelligent species should be found occupying an artificial biosphere which completely surrounds its parent star."

Dyson feels that if we accept this argument, we should not only search for intelligent life in the vicinity of visible stars. We might expect to find the most capable and advanced life occupying a dark sphere having a diameter about equal to that of the earth's orbit. Hidden inside would be their thoroughly harnessed, captive sun. Such a system would radiate energy at a rate equal to that of the blanketed star; however, the wave lengths would be in the far infrared below the threshold of ordinary visibility.

Using existing instruments, we could search for such infrared stars. Similar radiation from Mars and Venus

172

has been received and measured to calculate their surface temperatures. Dyson has proposed that we should undertake to look for these dark objects with our present telescopes, and he suggests that the chances for success of such a search might be very much improved if it were coupled with a parallel program to detect electronic signals.

A few scientists have pointed out that a number of the old myths and legends mention strange visitors from other worlds. It has even been suggested that the records should be searched to see if concrete evidence of such visits can be found. Frank Drake has drawn attention to the first three chapters of Ezekiel, in the Old Testament, where a strange story is recorded of how Ezekiel is met by four winged animals who carry him off to the Israelites. There is also an ancient legend of Sumer, certainly one of the oldest of civilizations, which concerns a strange fish-like creature who came out of the sea and taught the local people how to do many new things.

Some have pointed out that all these visitations occurred in the old days when the products of superstition and undisciplined imagination were almost as acceptable as the clearly visible truth. Except for the flying-saucer stories which have yet to be substantiated by any physical souvenirs, there has been a dearth of recent tales of visitors from foreign planets.

Dr. Carl Sagan has suggested that if we have indeed had visitors from other civilizations, they may possibly have left relics or other artifacts behind which were intended for use on later visits. He points out that such relics would probably be hidden away in remote locations so that we would not find and disturb them. Sagan has also suggested that such visitors may have established a base on some isolated body such as the moon which could be used every thousand years or so while they waited for us to awaken. He recommends that these ideas be kept in mind by the first and planetary explorers.

Physics, as we understand it today, would appear to limit severely the possibility of visitors from outer space because of the long travel time and the vast amount of fuel needed. However, our appreciation of these natural laws is of most recent origin, and there is no reason to believe that we have more than the most crude and rudimentary understanding of them at present. No scientist would argue that we know all the universal laws. Perhaps there are ways of conquering the great shackle of distance which we know nothing about.

Because of the formalities and conventions which have developed in our tastes over the years, most visitors from outer space have been portrayed in science fiction as the equivalent of the western "heavy" or the fellow in the dark vest. Indeed, we are instinctively fearful when we consider the possibility of being invaded by spacemen, as was demonstrated in 1938 by the panic generated by Orson Welles' celebrated radio program based on H. G. Wells' *War of the Worlds*. Perhaps this is a hangover from our own past. We humans have not been noted for benevolence in dealing with the underdeveloped and less enlightened members of our own species.

Is it reasonable to suppose that visitors from highly developed civilizations on other planets would seek to harm us or enslave us?

Dr. R. N. Bracewell of Stanford University discussed this question some time ago during a lecture in Sydney, Australia. "Now it has been suggested," he said, "that we should be very careful about making contact with other civilizations because they may want gold or some other valuable mineral found here, or they may just want our beef cattle. But I do not think this is a serious risk because of the enormous cost of transporting material objects over interstellar distances. It is undoubtedly cheaper to synthesize steak from its elements or to be a vegetarian than to import meat from another star . . . The most interesting item to be transferred from star to star is information, and this can best be done by radio."

NASA established a Committee on Long-Range Studies in 1960 to attempt to forecast some of the problems which might arise from our investigations in space. In a report submitted a year later, the committee did not rule out the possibility of harm resulting from our contact with advanced civilizations, even though our only

174

communication was by radio. In part, the report stated: "Anthropological files contain many examples of societies, sure of their place in the universe, which have disintegrated when they have to associate with previously unfamiliar societies espousing different ideas and different ways of life; others which survived such an experience usually did so by paying the price of changes in values and attitudes and behavior."

There are a number of reasons, however, why we can approach the coming of our ability to communicate with other technical life with a certain degree of confidence. These advanced societies have probably developed bombs and other lethal devices which are at least equal to the terrifying capability of ours. Yet they have survived. This indicates that they have succeeded in sublimating or disciplining many of the more predatory biological urges which we have yet to conquer. We will undoubtedly be safer in their company than they will be in ours, even though by comparison we are nothing more than rude barbarians.

Attempting to contact other intelligent life is a mature activity, requiring sociological advancement of a high order, as well as an advanced technical capability. It will not be undertaken by beings who are primarily motivated by money or power or conquest—or the local equivalents thereof. The basic drives for such a quest are those which reach to the very mainspring of intellectual progress: curiosity, thirst for knowledge, the desire to communicate with others.

Man has conquered the earth and is now truly master of all on its surface—except perhaps himself. The next step must surely lead outward from this small sphere, and just as surely man must take it if he is to continue to move ahead. Historically, the static forms have not been able to maintain a favorable status.

The scientists who are interested in a program to contact extraterrestrial intelligent life sometimes call themselves "intellexobiologists." They are not presently lobbying for more money in Washington for a new and more expensive Project Ozma, because they feel that a great deal of background work must be done before a full-scale program is justified.

First of all, we must explore the moon and Mars. The existence of life materials on either of these bodies will provide an excellent clue to the situation on other moons and planets.

We must proceed with the orbital telescope programs and the project to place a manned orbital laboratory in space. These programs will surely result in finding many more planetary systems which will strengthen the argument for life in other solar systems.

Beyond this, we will ultimately find use for an orbiting radio telescope observatory with a large receiving antenna, perhaps 1,000 feet in diameter. Such a station, using correlation techniques, will be able to detect the routine radio traffic on the planets of scores of nearby stars—if such traffic generates anything like the signal densities found on the earth.

As Frank Drake recently said in an editorial in the magazine, *Astronautics and Aeronautics*: "The *pièce de résistance* of the space program—the search for extraterrestrial intelligent life—appears to await the serving of some important appetizers. If the biochemistry of the solar system and the abundance of planetary systems turn out as we expect, stand back! Suddenly a search for other civilizations will be the most obvious, sensible, and widely supported program in scientific history."

At this moment we are aware of only one planet which sustains that charmed "chemical delicacy" known as life. When we speak there is no one to answer but ourselves. We are indeed lonely voyagers, surrounded by huge forces which we cannot control, bounded by limits of time and distance which we can only vaguely comprehend. The little we know of our true relationship to the vast universe has been scratched out bit by precious bit, at great labor, from the surrounding dark.

This is the human estate.

What are the future prospects? We will surely continue to learn more and more, faster and faster. But there is a far distance to go, and for you and me time is much too short. We need guides who know the trail and can speed the way to enlightenment. And this is why it is worthwhile to search for other intelligent life in the universe. The possibility of communication with distant worlds offers the most exciting opportunity for human enrichment in our time.

GLOSSARY

Subject	Definition
Subject	*Definition*
adenine	The base chemical of DNA, a basic building block of life which contains the information on heredity which is passed from one generation to the next.
algae	Rudimentary plants containing chlorophyll but having no roots, stems or leaves.
analog language	A language in which each utterance expresses a complete thought and which is not made up of discrete bits as is digital language.
angular momentum	The product of the moment of inertia of a body and its angular speed.
angular resolution	The ability of a telescope to distinguish between targets which are close together.
anti-matter	Matter with a charge opposite to that of normal matter. When matter and anti-matter collide, both may disappear.
asteroid	One of many small celestial bodies revolving around the sun, most of the orbits being between those of Mars and Jupiter.
atmosphere	The body of gases surrounding a planet.
bacteria	A one-celled microorganism containing no chorophyll.
binary code	A code composed of a combination of entities, each of which can assume one of two possible states.
binary star	One of a system of two stars revolving around each other.
biosphere	The transition zone between earth and atmosphere within which most forms of terrestrial life are found.
biplane	An airplane with two fixed wings, usually one above the other.
BMEWS	Ballistic Missile Early Warning System.
carbon dioxide-oxygen cycle	An atmospheric conversion cycle by which animals and planets mutually support each other.

Subject	Definition
carbonaceous chondritic meteorites	Small, black, soot-like meteorites containing material with organic characteristics.
cathode-ray screen	A screen which glows when cathode rays strike its surface. A TV receiver contains a cathode-ray screen.
comets	A body with a star-like nucleus and usually a long, luminous tail.
contrails	A visible trail of ice particles or water vapor left behind an aircraft or rocket.
cosmos	The universe considered as a harmonious, orderly system.
dermo-optical perception (DOP)	The ability to perceive an object with parts of the body other than the eyes.
digital language	A language made up of discrete digits or bits. Digital language is much more adaptable than analog language.
DNA	Deoxyribonucleic acid. The building block of life substances which contains heredity information passed from generation to generation.
doppler effect	The frequency shift caused by objects moving toward or away from an observer. As the target moves toward us the frequency is increased, as it moves away the reverse is true.
dualistic theory of planetary evolution	A theory of creation involving collision or near collision between two or more suns.
eclipse	The apparent cutting off of light from one celestial body by another which passes between it and the observer.
electromagnetic spectrum	The array of electromagnetic radiations from the short cosmic rays through the long gamma rays.
electron microscope	A microscope using electrons as an illuminating source instead of light.
enzyme	An organic substance produced by a living organism which produces changes in other organic substances.
evolutionary pecking order	Animals arranged in the order of their evolutionary progress.
exobiology	The study of living things beyond the earth.
extra-sensory perception (ESP)	The ability to perceive something without reliance on the known senses.
favorable opposition	The relative position of two orbiting celestial bodies when they are closest together.

Subject	Definition
Feulgen reaction	A reaction produced by a chemical which colors or stains DNA.
fossils	Hardened remains or traces of ancient animal or plant life.
frequency	The number of vibrations or cycles per unit of time.
galaxies	A cluster or grouping of millions of stars.
gamma ray	Radiation similar to X-rays but of shorter wave length.
greenhouse effect	The heating effect of the atmosphere caused by its absorption of short waves which are then re-emitted as longer (infrared) rays.
homo sapiens	That most marvelous of all creations—man.
hydrocarbons	Compounds of hydrogen and carbon, often products of living things.
hydrogen emission frequency	The frequency (about 1420 megacycles) at which hydrogen emits energy as its electrons change orbits.
infra-red	The long wave lengths of light (heat) just below the threshold of visibility.
intellexobiologists	Scientists who are searching for extraterrestrial intelligent life.
ionization	The process by which an atom loses or gains one or more electrons.
ionosphere	The outer layers of the earth's atmosphere extending beyond the stratosphere and consisting of ionized gases.
J-Band Life Detector	A detector of proteins which will be used in the search for life on Mars.
jamming	Disruption of electronic signals by use of artificial means.
knuckle of a curve	The point at which the curve changes direction rapidly.
laser	A device for amplifying light using stimulated emission.
learning curve	Increase in learning as a function of time.
light years	About 6 trillion miles, the distance which light will travel in one year at a rate of 186,272 miles per second.
lunar excursion module (LEM)	The capsule in which astronauts will descend to the moon's surface from a lunar orbiting satellite.
main sequence star	A star which is in the stage of development when energy is emitted by the thermonuclear reaction of its hydrogen.
Malthusian principle	The theory developed by Thomas Malthus that population increases as a geometric

179

Subject	Definition
	progression while the means to support life moves upward as an arithmetic progression.
Mark One Eyeball	The faculty of human sight still our most reliable means of finding objects.
maser	A device for amplifying microwave radiation using stimulated emission.
mass ratio	The ratio of the mass of the propellant charge of a rocket to the total mass of the rocket.
mass spectrometer	A device for detecting the presence of amino acids which will be used to search for life on Mars.
monistic theory of planetary evolution	A theory of planetary creation whereby planets are spun off in some manner from their parent stars.
multivator	A device for detecting life substances which will be used to search for life on Mars.
nebula	A celestial cloud of stars or gaseous material.
nitrogen cycle	The process by which nitrogen is returned to the soil by the decay of living things.
occultation	The disappearance of one celestial body behind another.
Optical Rotary Dispersion Profile Indicator	A device for detecting life substances which will be used in Martian exploratory experiments.
parabolic reflector antenna	A radio reflector antenna whose surface is in the shape of a paraboloid.
parallax	The angular change in the position of an object when viewed from two different vantage points.
parametric amplifier	Extremely sensitive electronic amplifiers used in radio telescope receivers.
parsec	A unit of length equal to the distance from the sun to a point having a parallax of 1 second (3.262 light years).
payload	The amount of useful load (astronauts or experiments) carried by a space craft.
phosphates	Substances containing phosphorus.
photo-electric cell	A device which converts light energy into electric current.
photometer	An instrument for measuring the intensity of light.
photo-synthetic bacteria	Bacteria which use energy from the sun in their life processes.
pitch	The apparent audio frequency of a signal.

Subject	Definition
polymers	Large aggregations of complex molecules arranged in a specific order.
psychokinesis	The attempt to shape events by thinking about them, such as mind-over-matter experiments.
quasi stellar radio source or quasar	Newly discovered distance sources of radio energy which radiate incredible power.
radar	A device which measures directions and distances by pulsing energy and receiving its reflection from a target.
radio telescope	A sensitive instrument for detecting distant electromagnetic signals.
rotational velocity	The angular velocity at which a celestial object is rotating.
sceptron	A device for converting sound waves to light for the purpose of analysis.
sonar	A device for transmitting sound energy and receiving target reflections underwater.
spectrometer	An instrument for reducing light to its basic components for the purpose of analysis.
spectrum analysis	The process of analyzing the spectrum obtained from a spectrometer.
sun	A celestial body which emits large quantities of light and heat.
symbiosis	The process by which animals and plants have co-operated to maintain the atmospheric balance.
thought transference	The attempt to transfer the thoughts of one person to another without use of the known senses.
troposphere	The lowest layer of atmosphere between the earth and the stratosphere.
ultra-violet	The short waves of light just beyond the threshold of visibility.
useful consciousness	The amount of time during which an astronaut can do useful work when he is unprotected in space.
Van Allen belt	A belt of intense particle radiation around the earth beginning at an altitude of about 250 miles.
vectored	Aircraft being directed from one point to another by a ground station.
Vidicon Microscope	A microscope with a television camera attached to be used in the exploration of Mars.
visual magnitude	The apparent brightness of a star measured in the light spectrum.

Subject	Definition
water cycle (hydrological cycle)	The cycle by which the water evaporates from the oceans, is transferred by the atmosphere and rained down upon the land.
Wolf Trap	A device for detecting life to be used in the exploration of Mars.
X-rays	Electromagnetic rays of extremely short length.

INDEX

183